A LETTER TO MYSELF

Françoise Mallet-Joris

A
LETTER TO MYSELF

Translated by PATRICK O'BRIAN
from the French

FARRAR, STRAUS & COMPANY

NEW YORK

A LETTER TO MYSELF

PART ONE

THE COOL ROOM with its tiled floor. Outside, sun-baked fields. Apple-trees: cows. Summer. A visitor.

"What are you doing now?"

"I am writing a novel."

"*Another*," says Lucien. "I don't believe in the novel any more. Nor in writing either, for that matter."

"Don't you?"

"In twenty years time no one will read anything but English."

"Really?"

"In thirty years they will do nothing but watch television."

"And then what?"

"Comic strips. Comic strips, I give you my word. People will no longer be able to read anything else. So, you see, when you tell me you are writing another novel . . ."

"It slays you?"

He makes a little movement of withdrawal—no, it does not 'slay him': he would not go so far as that (in any case the expression does not suit him at all); but still . . . My confidence surprises him, or rather grieves him. He writes too, of course; but with no illusions.

". . . just for myself . . ."

The cool room. Through the small-paned window, a broad

view of apple-trees and cows. A great stretch of baked fields, reddish-brown and grey. Colour-killing drought. In Flanders the fields are green, the sunlight golden, the clouds round, filled and ringed about with light, a Louis xɪv halo, because of the moisture that loads the heavy air.

". . . because of the moisture . . ."

"Indeed?" he says, vaguely.

It does not interest him : the only thing that does fundamentally interest him is writing. Literature, and the bewailing of literature's dismal end. "After all, you must admit that when you sit there, gazing at your cows, and calmly tell me that you are writing a new novel, as if you were telling me that the wheat was growing well . . ."

Lucien is a romantic. He is a romantic in spite of his position as a public servant, his rather prim ways and his dismal prophecies.

"But come, I could hardly wring my hands as I tell you about it, could I ?"

"In short," he says, in the same tone that he must employ when he is questioning a dunce in the examination for moving up to the next form (exasperated mildness, utter certainty of the pupil's worthlessness, but the resignation of one who will do his duty to the last), "in short, for your part you believe that writing has a future?"

"I don't know. I don't give a damn. I never ask myself whether it has or not. As you put it, I gaze at my cows, and I write."

I am not really as sure of myself as I seem. And all these cows do not mean anything at all. But this kind of question seems pointless to me : it bores me. And I rather like making game of Lucien.

"And if nobody reads you any more, you will not . . . give a damn?"

"I'll simply write in English, that's all."

"They won't read that either for long."

"I shall write for the television."

"Perhaps you will do comic strips?"

"Why not?"

That vexes him. Yet he ought to like comic strips, for he has ventured into surrealism. However, he does not. But in any case everything here tends to vex him. The cows (is it reasonable to come to see people in Normandy at the very height of summer if you cannot stand cows?), the children, the novels that I have planned, the canvasses drying, face to the wall; to say nothing of the cider, which gives him a stomach-ache.

I do admit that there is something a little too perfect in this summer afternoon, in the charged silence of this room, the gleam of the polished tiles, and outside the drone of insects that might be the sound of the heat itself. The fruit that has dropped too early is ripening on the wicker racks; there is the shrilling of the summer crickets; everything falls into swags of classical verse. Vexing, for a former surrealist—one stuffed with principles, like all the former surrealists I have ever met. It all lacks a touch of hell. It is all too perfect, too carefully done, too 'colour-supplement'. The Soviet artist, surrounded by blond heads and dreaming of his furrows. Everything that Lucien dislikes.

But what does he like? One may well ask, when one sees the way he lives : he is austere, he moves in the fashionable world (the one does not exclude the other), well-dressed in a somewhat funereal manner (half-way between the dandy and the under-taker's mute), with condemnation ready on his lips : a contemp-tuous, frugal prophet, dressed in clothes made to measure—even his shirts, a luxury that fills us with amazement.

Really, one has some friends, and when one comes to think about it it is impossible to tell how one ever became friendly with them. A chance meeting, a habit one falls into, and there is Lucien, thirty-five years old, a frigid poet, a teacher of Latin (the dead language suits him well), coming to see me regularly every month in Paris, every summer in the country : he utters a few dreary prophecies, looks round him with tolerant disapprobation (rather as *Le Monde* might do) and goes away after the meal, awkward and spreading awkwardness, with his brief-case under his arm and old Sade jostling the red-pencilled exercises in it. A strange world, Lucien's. An abstract world, class-rooms, drawing-rooms, an elegant little flat in a part of the town that is just like him—deserted, proper, funereal . . . They tell me Lucien is a good poet.

Knowing him, I am quite aware that my own world (cows, children, canvasses and this novel that has been begun) must seem just as strange to him. He too must say to himself "Really one has some friends . . ." And we go on conversing from one side of a chasm to another.

Somewhere there must be a misunderstanding : but how can it be done away with? Maybe Lucien and I really are friends after all? But what can one do about it? Lucien's perfect manners make any direct assault on my part impossible. 'Your children are splendid . . .' he says. Or, 'What a charming place you have.'

Sickened, amused, I see myself as Lucien must see me. It might really be an article in *Paris-Match*. Myself among the cows, under the apple-trees. And one picture : just one. Jacques, my husband, a little farther off, in a field, carefully dishevelled, in front of his easel. Blond heads in picturesque attitudes before *the old farmhouse to which she goes in search of the quiet she needs for* . . . I should look very well, with my dog, and, this summer, with my fourth child inside me. At least, that is what the photo-graphers say.

"Just in the door, perhaps. These old steps . . ."

"Rather commonplace, don't you think, darling? Maybe pick-ing up a crying child . . . Would you pretend to be crying, sweetie-pie?"

Delighted, my daughter launches into the most spirited postur-ing.

"What about another one? The kitchen? The fireside is not bad, either. Sitting by the fire . . ."

"In August, darling? Come!"

"What about August? It rains in August sometimes, doesn't it? After all, we are in Normandy."

"Yes, but everybody knows that this year . . ."

"All right, all right, just as I was saying . . . Counting your fruit, then. That will be pretty in colour . . ."

I can see it all as clearly as though I were there. Gérard Géry, who always promises to send me photographs and never does; the over-excited children; the photographers who, contrary to their reputation, are delightful, and take advantage of this day in the country to fool about in the hay and climb trees. They buy the children lollipops and they are real *buddies* (buddies whom one will never see again, however, for they never send the same ones twice)—I see it all, and it is all perfectly charming and it all swims in the pervasive falsity of parties in the country. And this calm, poised Mallet-Joris, these novels, children, COWS . . . It is clear that Lucien is obsessed by them. He darts stealthy, frightened glances in their direction. To him they seem symbolic of the way Jacques and I are rooted in the earth.

"And they really do not hinder your painting?" he says to Jacques.

"What?" asks Jacques, who never listens when other people are talking.

"These cows . . ."

"What cows?" asks Jacques uneasily, as if he expected to see one in the room. "Oh, yes. The cows . . . But I don't paint cows . . ."

I feel that if he dared Lucien would say, "And these children?" (for in the scale of unpleasant things he places the children next to the cows); but he does not dare. Jacques is always in the clouds, and perhaps Lucien suspects him of being capable of replying, "What children?" An abstract painter will stop at nothing. So he does no more than murmur, "Well, here you are, beautifully settled in . . ." and he accepts a glass of cider, because of the heat; though he makes a little prophetic face as he does so (but no, he will not take off his coat).

Yet God knows we are not at all what is ordinarily called 'beautifully settled in'. There is still no bathroom (and the children make the very most of it not to wash), the walls are bare, the beds uncommonly hard, and shelves take the place of the entirely non-existent furniture; but I understand Lucien perfectly well. What he means is, "In your house on the top of the hill, with your children, your cows [I shall never be able to make him understand that these cows do not belong to me—I wish they did], your novels and your pictures, you are beautifully settled in life."

It is but right to add that he qualifies this opinion with a sceptical "And after all who knows but you may be right?" which carries about as much conviction as the well-known "It is always the best who leave us" which people say at death-beds—the dead having become harmless—and which gives me the same sort of malaise, the same disagreeable uneasiness.

I must admit that it is unusual for me to stop feeling a kind of uneasiness. In conversation, at dinners, in daily life. All these uneasinesses, *constraints,* mount up, and I am not happy until I have been able to discover a reason for them. Sometimes I succeed in a couple of seconds : sometimes it has needed years before a moment's perplexity, which was sticking like a little knot in my memory, has—sometimes by mere chance—dissolved and faded away.

Now this picture that is forming in the eyes, the rather small eyes, of Lucien, the distant, reserved friend, talented poet and conscientious public servant, is going to make another little knot. And how odd it is that this picture should bring the distinguished, sceptical Lucien and *Paris-Match*'s excited, hearty, platinum-blond photographer together.

"We can make something of you," says the photographer to

me, in an ingratiating tone. "Besides, women are always easier; particularly when they have children."

I contemplate this Mallet-Joris who 'always looks well' in all weathers and in all surroundings, if only she will make a little effort. Under a Christmas tree (*it is a pity that you should have cut your hair: the bun looked more . . . how shall I put it . . . .*) 'Yes, how will you put it?' I see her doing one of the children's homework or at the bedside of her latest baby (*you know it is the fourth? Take the others leaning over the cradle—that will look perfectly sweet . . . What about the caption? She has been divorced twice, you know. But that only goes to show that she likes marriage, doesn't it? It wouldn't do: think of the women readers . . .*) and it seems to me that we have very little in common.

I see her smiling charmingly on page three (not on the cover—that does not come yet) making pancakes on pancake day—rather an awkward young woman (not that there is any harm in that: it is human), something of a 'people's' writer, rather preoccupied with the picturesque; a good-hearted creature with a big family, and not devoid of a certain talent that can instantly be seen to be reactionary, sanguine and *wholesome*; a woman who can cook (which is true), who wears gloves to go to Mass (which is not); quantities of virtues, her heart on her sleeve, an unparalleled knitter; rather stupid, but with a stupidity that pleases unsophisticated readers—"Here's a woman who does not make a fuss just because she writes"—and others, who are naïve in another way and who acquire a taste for her as they might for home-made bread, "She knows nothing whatever about anything at all, but she is quite delightful."

Poor Mallet-Joris. Yet after all I would rather she did not manage to get into this medallion, this family portrait, tossing a pancake. Even though she does make them every time pancake day comes round—for that very reason, indeed. "Oh, please do. Be kind. I'm sure you won't disappoint us—you will have two full pages : perhaps a cover! After all, there is nothing discreditable about tossing a pancake."

No; there is not. Nor in spending the summer gazing at the cows, nor in cooking, nor in writing a new novel without wringing one's hands. Nothing discreditable; but something just a little irritating nevertheless. I understand Lucien; but he is wrong in blaming the cows, the children and marriage. After all, his little schoolgirls at the Lycée X come to much the same thing as my apple-trees and horned cattle. He says they give him the independence that a writer needs, that is a salary and holidays. Very well. But if my nails itch when I read the throbbing story that asserts it is possible to be both *writer and mother* and cites me as an example, then it must set Lucien's teeth on edge when a glossy magazine tells him, "this humble little schoolmaster with greying hair may be the greatest writer in France". Cows or exercise-books, we are both in the same boat.

Or at least, in the same catalogue—the catalogue that photographers and journalists must certainly look through when they need something to fill a gap on page three. You can find anything you want in it, from the gossip item to the page in colour. Straight away you see what picture to take and what story-line to follow. For Lucien : dark class-rooms, solitude-leprous-walls, wanderings in Paris, correction of a pupil's exercise—the modesty of this task. And if it is pathos you want: little man, hardly ridiculous at all, alone on a bridge, turning splendid phrases in his head. And if it is the *human* : close-up of spectacles and the startled air of the intellectual surprised. It is child's play.

If you want to make him an object of compassion, you must take your subject from below—his blinking eyes without spectacles, the line of his thin lips blurred, an air of unconquerable youthfulness . . . On the other hand from above you have the hatchet face, the scornful curve of the mouth, now a strong line again . . . instead of being pathetic, the solitude has become contemptuous. He despises mankind, lives among his books, feeds on

15

Seneca and should be taken in profile, in front of a Roman bust, like M. de Montherlant. You only have to choose. It is very convenient. For him, solitude, twilight, spectacles and statues; for me, children, country or a café in Paris, pancakes or knitting, cows . . .

No : that is quite enough of cows. They are beginning to haunt me as much as Lucien himself. Alas, one can escape from cows. Can one escape from

catalogues ?

The captions of photographs, interviews with the best of intentions, it all reminds me (like the bitter-sweet remarks that I can almost hear coming from Lucien's mouth : "I have seen Françoise : oh yes, indeed; the country, the children; she is happy . . ." And then the cows loom up again) of the awkwardness that one feels faced with a publicity release. *The theme of this book . . .* The theme, to be sure. And the characters. *The principal character, X, is an elderly man who* . . . Why not? Do I believe in the theme, though? Indeed, it amuses me to say to myself, "I have written, I am going to write, a book that will tell this story : *A man is writing his diary and then . . . A girl wants to inherit from her father and all of a sudden . . .*"

The more the plot is a 'plot' the better I like it. Up to the point of laughing at it a little, so as to set it apart from the rest and so that it should not fool me too much : *a king's favourite* . . . Yes, I love that. And the characters! Yet they too come out of a catalogue. *He was a man of about forty, with a worn, lined face.* Writing something as plain as that does literally give me a feeling of exaltation. Only . . . how shall I put it? I no more believe in it than I believe in the F.M.J. who *gets up at six, and at the crack of dawn goes and sits in a remote café where every day she begins writing at the same time, surrounded by the rattling of the crockery and the smell of disinfectant on the floor.*

True enough, appearances are all against me. I do get up at

six. I do go and work in the café. I really do have four children, and I spend my summers in the little farmhouse on the hillside . . . As Lucien says, *I am happy*. And I am writing a new novel. In actual fact I am still at the stage of making notes and waiting for something to swim up to the surface; and perhaps that was the reason for the uneasiness that I felt when I said "I am writing a new novel". And when Lucien says, "You are writing a new novel", it also seems to me that he is rather over-simplifying, that he is seeing things in a false light, just as the *Paris-Match* photographers, or the photographers of any other weekly of that kind might see them.

Furthermore, what irritates me is not the fact that he forms a wrong opinion of me; it is rather that his opinion should be so nearly right that it takes on all the appearance of the right opinion, and that it differs from it only by a shade, a hair's breadth, an almost nothing. And this shade is very like that which for me separates the beginning of a novel—the moment when I say to myself "I am going to write the story of a man who . . ."—from the moment when, two years after beginning the work, I leave off, hoping that this book is after all something other than the *story of a man who*.

What then? Should I say to Lucien, "Oh, I don't believe in writing all that much, you know"? That would not be true either. For I must admit that since I was a child I have felt a positive passion, a feeling in which delight and distress, patience and impatience, are all mingled, for watching, describing, transforming and not transforming—in short, for writing. I feel it strongly when I am there, sitting in a café (I cannot get away from that picture) rather at a loss; and almost without thinking of it, so as to pass the time and by way of amusement and practice too, I make notes in my diary upon

anyone at all

A little old man, for example—yet not so old, either; it is the effect of the beret. He is reading a right-wing paper and he complains because his coffee is luke-warm. "Boiling, I said!" His poor little peremptory voice. Each of his thoughts has a political opinion over it, like the loose-covers on furniture.

He is an ex-service man; he attends Armistice Day parades; he loves his family and makes its life scarcely worth the living; he talks about the working classes; he talks about the French sense of restraint and moderation; he talks about the greatness of France; he talks about French trees and the French soil; and he has a decoration.

He quotes Péguy (three lines), he is not-at-all-against-the-Jews-but—in short he is really anyone at all. Sickeningly ordinary. His country house! (A bungalow.) His relationship with his children! If he is a bachelor he replaces Péguy by 'his old Montaigne' (the Nelson edition or the old family copy on his bedside table, which he never opens). In this case he is more of a sceptic and he is less worked up, and the beret takes on a more bohemian, almost an anarchistic, value; he likes saying, "As for torture, that has always gone on", and he torments his old servant, who pays him back in his own coin (both varieties of this species are tormentors). He may also have the complete works of Chateaubriand or Anatole France, bound in calf, in his library; and he may collect something.

If he is a bachelor, he is not very clean. His collars . . . If he is married, he washes in cold water, so as to be able to annoy his children : "In my time we did not have all these conveniences and . . ." These conveniences, however, go no further than a bathroom that has never been repainted since the first child was born, and whose geyser works only on red-letter days.

Anyone at all. Two perfectly probable varieties of a single species which, with inward apologies to M. François Mauriac for the 'base four-letter word', one is obliged to call 'the old c——s'. It should be observed that there is no ulterior political motive in this description of mine. It is true that the right wing is rich in old c——s. The left, on the whole, is more attractive to the young c——s : that is all. (And there the base word readily takes on the feminine gender, likes going to bed late and hitting the ceiling with indignation, and is progressive to the point of abortion. The mental masturbation that goes on every day in the left bank cafés on the subject of under-developed countries and police atrocities reaches Babylonian proportions. But for all that, if you try to find a volunteer for sticking up posters, you will be astonished.)

Besides, they are quite pleasant creatures, these fierce old grandfathers who want their coffee piping hot and hate the North African and the tax-gatherer impartially, and these trousered young women, who are really touching when they cannot get over a little misfortune in love, which can happen in spite of contraceptives.

I say anyone at all and I am talking about that anyone at all who is to be seen in cafés. Well then, when I have noted down these stories of the geyser, and when I have taken a certain mechanical pleasure in seeing how utterly unchanging they are and how regularly, mathematically, recurrent (together with the stories about joint ownership, of the flooding of the downstairs neighbour, of the pregnant servant-girl and the car that stopped), everything remains to be done. I love analysing what constitutes the mechanism of everyday life. I like to feel that this knowledge will be useful to me (and I assure you that trouble with geysers takes up at least as much space in people's lives as trouble caused by love or the war in Algeria) but I feel strongly that it all amounts to no more than theatrical props, and perhaps to alibis. And I feel that the little old man (yet not so old; it is the effect of the beret) whom I could describe so easily and who would then be *so well drawn* (as the hairdresser's apprentice says—the one who buys the books that win the literary prizes), that the little old man would for me too be a prop and an alibi, if I stopped there.

If I set out upon this line of thought, it is because Lucien's remark, and still more the exemplary and rather irritating image of myself that it reflects, makes me conscious of a crystallization that has slowly been going on inside me since—God knows how long : for ever, perhaps, but I have only lately known about it. Now at this point my reader grows uneasy, and I with him. All this introductory stuff, this plot which is not a plot, these alibi-characters . . . can it be that this new novel is a *New Novel*? One of these novels that has no plot, no characters, no punctuation?

Oh, if punctuation irked me, or plot, or characters, I should certainly throw them overboard, and that without supposing that just because I do without the full-stops and commas I have accomplished a literary revolution. But the truth is they do not irk me. I am going to write a novel with a plot and characters. It is an old tool, no doubt; but it is one that can still be useful. Useful to me, at all events. I have nothing, absolutely nothing, against the new gadgets. Some of them are very handy, and I should make use of them myself without hesitation in case of need. *In case of need*; there is the whole question. Although it can make one furious not to be able to lay one's hand upon the tool one needs (*Finnegans Wake* was a splendid testimony to this fury, quite a long time ago), it seems to me that by confusing one's instrument with one's work one risks ruining oneself, like that character of Huxley's, by buying ever more complicated machines and spending one's life gazing at them, while the paper remains virgin white.

I say this because I do not like mixing the floor-cloths and the towels : a housewife's fad, no doubt. But I love tools, my own and other people's. And a beautiful, well-assembled machine delights me, so long as it is not only a machine. What is annoying me today is the fact of being something of 'a mere machine' in Lucien's eyes. Machine for making babies, for making novels, for making conversation according to an established ritual. And yet there is nothing insulting about that. How hard to please I have become. For I remember when I was little my somewhat uneasy admiration for those grown-ups who always seemed to know what they ought to do or reply—indeed, it was life itself that seemed to know for them, life, which they called upon to bear witness when they said, "You know me; with my nature I cannot agree . . ." or "At his age, there was clearly no question of . . ." Everything seemed to have been settled, once and for all, at some earlier time (*for Renée's marriage, I can* only *wear my blue dress*).

Apparently it all worked without any grinding, without hesitation, well oiled, well run-in, with a smooth sliding of the mechanism and the words. How I admired that perfectly tuned combination, those thrusts that were answered by other symmetrical thrusts, those justly-punished transgressions (*I cut her dead, as you may imagine*), those civilities which were necessarily replied to by other civilities (the phrase *to pay back a dinner* gave me a lively arithmetic satisfaction. And *to give* a dinner, too, since I knew that in the fullness of time this dinner would be paid back). How I admired, yes, how I admired those carefully kept accounts of a touching bourgeoisie (*she does not dress as she should; the wife of a president of the court of appeal ought* . . .), those codes of law, those scales, that splendid

machine for living

How attractive it was, and reassuring; but still rather hard, rather puzzling for my eight-year-old, ten-year-old, twelve-year-old head. It seemed to me that you only had to choose, once and for all, and all the rest would follow automatically—the clothes to wear, the words to say. A knack, a way of doing the thing, like learning how to ride a bicycle. But something told me that I did not have this knack. And this doubt followed me throughout all my childhood.

Adolescence caused this modest little anxiety to lose its importance : there were so many other things to hanker after ! And then suddenly, because of the heat of an afternoon, because of a house of my own, of a lull in the misdeeds of the children, because of a happy love, of a novel begun and of a friend who was not so much of a friend as all that, I was wondering whether that Mallet-Joris who, according to the *Paris-Match* photographs and in Lucien's mind, seemed so thoroughly to have found her machine for living, was not really myself after all.

Why make a fuss or a scene over it? After all, there is nothing discreditable in writing novels, having babies, marching in Armistice Day parades (no: my wires are crossed). Cows, pancakes, thick volumes and fair heads—a lifetime's programme, a perfectly running machine. A dash of ideology over it all to prevent it from being dull . . . Neither discreditable nor difficult. An excellent place in the catalogue.

And it does not even call for any effort. With maturity, the particular knack comes of itself. Even before maturity, sometimes. It is so easy that people line up to get into the catalogue. But getting out of it, why, that is another question. (And why should there be this revolt?) Because that would upset everything. In the first place 'they' would be cross, upset. *And we who had done so much for her!* The public—but just as much the neighbourhood, the family, one's office—there is a positive little world of people, all ready to be very much put out because one has changed one's role.

How about trying it? Yet how can you do so without falling into another trap just at hand? Yet suppose we do. It may well be that they smother the whole business: I buy a Jaguar, I appear at first nights, I write a pornographic book—none of it is any good; I still remain the symbol of motherly love, the "good little woman who does not look anything much and who cooks sweetbreads so admirably". Turning their eyes away from my low-necked dress they go on taking pictures of my children; they detect God and despair in my lewd essays; and as for my Jaguar, it is so that I can travel faster to the little farmhouse in Normandy where I spend my holidays, rather than in the open arms of the Ritz at Cannes. It goes on so long that in the end "the good little

22

woman who does not look anything much" makes the hairdresser's apprentice laugh. Finally, since after all nobody takes any interest in it any more, they will not even mention my thirty-third South American lover.

On the other hand, it may be that they will go into reverse. Nowadays everybody practises the 'slippery eel' technique "We always told you so: besides, didn't you know that she was divorced twice? The children? Accidents: mere accidents. And they were useful for her publicity. You only have to look at the film stars. They all have them. Nowadays you can't get anywhere without a baby. Or you have to announce that you are sterile and have yourself photographed holding babies smiling in your arms, with your eyes gazing wistfully into the distance. It's quite true, darling, I do assure you. They *hire* them. There are places where you go—I know it as a fact. But she has overdone it, you see. She has made a mess of the whole thing."

"Perhaps we could do something with it? A solid article, very psychological, very advice to the love-lorn. How did this mother of four turn into a vamp? It could be quite pathetic: we could show the breaking marriage, the neglected, suffering husband, the abandoned children with their far too luxurious toys. And it could end with a heart-throb, something like this, 'Pull yourself together, Françoise; your babies are stretching out their arms to you,' etc."

"Yes, perhaps we could. If the insect story does not come in, it might do. Rough out a draft."

a draft

I shall certainly have to make one myself for my new novel. There are quantities of things I want to talk about, but they have not found their pretext yet, nor their lead-in. As the catalogue would say, I am not with it yet.

I can *feel* what it is that I want to talk about perfectly well,

23

just as there in front of my window I can perfectly well see those two differently shaped and differently coloured fields (one draws away to the horizon, a pale field; while the other, a thick ochre, comes right up to my feet in a square, strong wave, rimmed round with the firm green of the hedge) whose perfect, sad harmony cannot possibly be conveyed in one word: I can *feel* what it is, but I do not yet *know* what it is. I must wait, sitting in front of the small-paned window of a garret bedroom, until this whirlwind has died down and I can select, discard, go down to the core . . . A whirlwind of images, stories, memories, short flashes, an apparently incoherent hodge-podge, but which for me is linked by a kind of unity that is my life itself and that for the moment I am powerless to break.

Powerless, since it is this very unity that is troubling my mind. Because of Lucien, because of the heat of the afternoon, because . . . Is this unity, *myself*, merely factitious? Are all these things, the age of thirty that I reached this year (those thirty unimaginable years of childhood), this house we bought at the time I won the Prix Fémina (that prize which was also a landmark), this profession, these children—are they all only the going-train of a machine for living and nothing more?

This anxiety also stirs up quantities of images: I must wait, go on waiting. It does not matter. For this, if for nothing else, I have learnt patience. Illness would have been enough to teach me, even if it had not been for childhood, which is also a disease. So I shall spend days behind this window: perhaps weeks. Then one image more brilliant than the rest will come to the surface: grasp it, spread it out on the desk and wonder how to translate it into words, just as I am wondering how I can seize the delicate harmony of that three-sided field, with its yellow that is scarcely yellow.

Make a plan. Make a plan even for this present train of thought. A draft dealing with truth and falsehood, for example. After all, I always come back to that. But how wearying it is!

How false it is, and how facile, this *speciality*—as much a speciality as the Poiré-Blanche chocolate éclairs. Here I am right back in the catalogue, the role, the theme.

My poor Mallet-Joris, you are playing their game! 'Follow the guide' and the trick is done; speech is silver, but falsehood is golden, and the reader, duly warned by you, by *you*, Mallet-Joris, is looking for the lie from the first page with the deep certainty of one looking for a murderer in a detective story. It might be anyone, but a murderer there is, and that is sure. You are turning out thrillers, Mallet-Joris; you are brewing the opium of the people. Sleep soundly, machine for living, machine for writing. You have an

alibi

Is falsehood an alibi? Plot an alibi? Perhaps. Still, a choice is not necessarily an alibi. Not choosing is also a choice. There is nothing more subjective than objectivity, oh Robbe-Grillet; and that fifty-three centimetre table whose dimensions you state so insistently, that table alone gives me an inner certainty that at home you wear a scarlet dressing-gown. Scarlet, Robbe-Grillet! Like Flaubert! Like Flaubert, too, that brown table to the left with a penknife-cut in it (another Bovary), that carefully unconscious but fundamentally so naïve and almost sentimental table, is yourself. And if you make use of the table, if you cannot leave it alone, why should I not make use of the lie? It is one of the only sins that still remain to us. As for the fine crimson sins of former days, nobody believes in them any more. What a loss for novelists! What

nostalgia!

Oh the innocent souls, the innocent days, when one damned

oneself for passion! I dream of them, those passions which were the subject of the great sermons of a former age. God, give us back your great childish sins of lust and anger and gluttony, and even the evergreen sin of avarice, which still stands with its proud head high.

To kill for shining toys! To perish body and soul in a great blazing fire of infantile desires, for a woman, a throne, money, an appointment as the keeper of a level-crossing! The sky obscured, the whole world filled by this single longing for a hundred thousand francs (you can see them already, finger them, eat them), by this obsession for one particular woman with a mole and one breast smaller than the other, or for a horse or a diamond!

Those passions were not alibis—they were not pallid papier mâché disguises. Or if they were they were genuine alibis. Poetical sinners and gluttonous sinners, there you all stand naked in front of God (which of you bothered with fancy-dress?) like children taken in the act, and your hand hides your privities, or your livers, once the seat of hearty rage, or your guts, swollen with gold and gluttony—those entrails that formerly delighted in their sin and that are knotted now with anguish. How God must love you in your simplicity, ingenuous sinners of the mediaeval damnations! The body swelled at the expense of the soul: it will grow thin and flaccid on the penitential diet of Purgatory. Peace, peace upon the privities and upon the guts: God gave them to you; He has taken them away. Now it is only a question of bringing the other mechanism into play, the one that is there, quite new, quite whole, and which has never been used. 'It is always like that,' God must think, compassionately watching the tiny efforts as they get into running order.

Yes, I dream of those guileless sins, flat, without background, those lives in strong, primary colours, and that ingenuous heraldic symbolism. Is it perhaps that simplicity which our coloured weeklies are trying to rediscover with such blundering pains?

The *Margaret and Tony—watch out for squalls!* headings are perhaps more things of a former day than products of the modern world, as the little old man in the beret says. Perhaps the good people said "X., Y. and Eleanor of Aquitaine—watch out for squalls!" Totem colours; symbols that have grown hollow, eaten out by the ants of time. The whole difference resides in this, that nobody believes in these old faded images any more. It is a way of passing the time, of forgetting the tax-gatherer, of dozing pleasantly: nobody believes in Margaret, nor in the sins. And no sins, no theme. Vicissitudes of fortune, that is all. Falsehood is the only sin that has done well: that alone would be reason enough to talk about it.

Vacuum sinning: it is everywhere. Communications, societies, distinctions and decorations, literary prizes and picturesque photographs, dear statesmen who are so kind as to be 'popular', cigar in mouth or hand to képi: whose string of little new hollow-headed gods (lighter than the old ones; like the coins, gods are devalued, too) give an evil chuckle and take up their dwelling among us, just like the lares of the good old thick-headed Romans. But if you ask me, those Romans were lying already. With all those generals about, really! For your part, do you believe in that one about Cincinnatus and his plough? There have been so many since then who have gone back to their plough with their pockets full, or with the expectation of being sent for from its tail. *Conversations around a Plough*: that would make a charming title, and I have half a mind to suggest it to Lucien, who reads Malraux. But he would not be with me.

If I could only make him understand that I have no desire to be a totem, no vocation for it, whatever the attendant rites may be. But one is always a totem for somebody, even if it is only oneself. Have I become a totem for myself? That is the question I am asking myself today. And why not? Where would be the harm? 'There is nothing discreditable about tossing a pancake . . .'

pancakes

Nothing. I return to my pancakes as Lucien to his cows, which have become the symbol of virtue and morality for him, just as for me these pancakes have become the vessels of falsehood or of truth. Stuffed pancakes, to some degree. It seems to me quite clear that there is something indecent about making a pancake (or dealing with a baby's napkins or picking apples) in front of a lens, even if in fact I pass my days doing just these things. Even if, and above all if, as I said before. Perhaps it is just that I lack naturalness?

Lucien's implied question of today has been hanging over me for some time. You cannot, without paying for it, be thirty years old, run a profession, have four children, a house in the country and the intention of starting a new novel. And of starting another after that one, and then another still . . . Without paying for it one cannot have the responsibility and perhaps the alibi of the worries about money and arrangements which these children bring with them; nor can one have one's political, religious, literary opinions—any opinions you like—without a corresponding quantity of questions and doubts which mount up in a corner like the letters that one will have to make up one's mind to answer one day. A correspondence with oneself, as it were. (A pun rich in meanings.) One day I shall certainly have to make up my mind to reply to myself. You cannot with impunity own a machine that is ready to work. The day comes when you are obliged to ask yourself what it is meant to do. If indeed it is meant to do anything. And if not . . .

We caught her making her children pancakes for—no, the traditional pancakes for pancake day. We asked her for her own personal recipe and you will find it at the bottom of the page. Why this obsession with pancakes? The journalists do not badger me, as you might suppose. The glory of literary prizes fades quickly, and it is only now and then that a woman's paper, running out of material, sends me an interviewer and a photographer. But I am utterly fascinated by the phenomenon of transmutation that takes place every time, turning the simplest word, the most ordinary movement, into the subtle paper lie. Want of innocence, if not want of naturalness. And this obsession with falsehood; I really must change the subject a little.

Suppose I talk about naturalness, for example? And innocence? About the ancient Greeks—the light and terrible Cora at the Terme in Rome, who certainly never knew what falsehood was? She cannot ever be loved enough, this smiling goddess who is unaware of her own divinity, who is surrounded by broad-shouldered, slim-waisted, rather short-legged males and who is pregnant with death. She is innocent: yes, as innocent as Frazer's Tahitians—one of the family climbs a palm tree, falls, breaks his neck and lies there stark dead: all the rest burst out laughing at something so very unexpected.

Present relevance of this theme. Nostalgia for this laughter. But can this laughter be copied? It can no more be copied than that daily action which loses all meaning in the photograph. 'The beauty of the primitive forces!' cry the philosophers and the lovers of our day, doing their best, with great swathes of quotations and draughts of whiskey, to return to a state of nature. The state of nature in which there is neither falsehood nor truth . . .

Perhaps that is where my subject really lies? From far down among the swirling images the great terrified forms from the Villa of the Mysteries stand out with a curious emphasis. Garden of Eden: absurd, unthinking terror, as drunk as joy; and which is joy, perhaps—does one ever know? Does one know yet? You can never really stand in the Garden of Eden again: you can only close your eyes to the outside world. And closing your eyes is not the same as being blind, and blinding yourself is not the same thing as being blind, even if you do strike in with a splendid poetic despair, delicately grasping Jocasta's gold and coral pin

(I can see it, a slightly over-elaborate brooch—frankly, in rather poor taste). By no effort of will can a poet ever make of himself a man blind from birth, wrapped in the protecting, stifling cocoon, the very womb of emptiness.

Why this subject? Why should the name of Georges Bataille and his *Expérience Intérieure* suddenly come to me like the name of some distant relative, some traveller from whom one has not heard and to whom one cannot write, but who flits across one's memory every now and then? Because of this nostalgia, no doubt; this kinship of nostalgia, this kinship of death, which I still feel like an old wound as I sit here behind my little panes, in my house, watching my children in my field, and my life spread out like a wave at my feet.

Nostalgia. They say that by asceticism Buddhists succeed in reaching the same luke-warm formless state of the new-born calf blinded by the farmer, the pathetic calf which turns its head this way and that and which sees, oh poet, nothing but your longed-for emptiness. In any case one knows that the Buddhist does not eat the flesh of the calf—this veal that has been so cunningly kept so white. But who will eat the Buddhist flesh, your flesh, oh poet-philosopher? Who will savour this lovingly-cooked emptiness? You? That at least is what you are looking forward to, with all your expert preparations. But calves do not eat veal: and you are to take notice, philosophers, that you will not profit by so much as even the smell of the state-of-nature dish that you are simmering over the well-banked fire of inward experience, even if you do happen to make a success of it. An end to this charming duality: you should content yourselves with being *he who is,* with not being—a task which the grocer at the corner of the street succeeds in perfectly well without the help of any asceticism. Poised between the lentils and the packets of Omo he *is* splendidly. He is void.

Nostalgia; childhood, emptiness, the birth of a thought, false-hood and truth, falsehood begetting truth, acknowledging, praising truth; the state of nature impossible to recover, the beauty of innocence, farewell to innocence : abstract words, concrete truths—in short, a reasonably noble theme. To be taken up with a certain amount of care. Preliminary reading, a notebook for quotations—perhaps a filing-cabinet. Not a novel, at any rate. The story of my life up until the present. The story of life and me up until the present. The story of my endeavour to live, my search for that ease in living, for that machine for living . . .

Too hard. I have not read enough. Mind too quickly tired of abstract words, too quickly surfeited. Too apt to exude images to be able to follow a train of reasoning through to the end. Too passionately eager to give body to every word, every little idea, to go far and fast. On the other hand, quite prudent. Weighs each word—sniffs at it. No : too early to write that book. But starting off from this nostalgia, this need of childhood, and of nothingness, and of the alibi, the savage innocence and the triumphal absurdity, I may perhaps turn this novel into the

portrait of Lambert

Because of the state of nature, and because Lambert never washes. However, he is no more dirty than the twisted old branch of a tree, full of earth, broken in some places and withered in others. He does not sweat, he scarcely eats at all, and his hair is very white. Just as truth begins with a lie, so dirtiness begins with washing.

Lambert is seventy-five, he weighs eight stone; he does not wash, he does not comb his hair; and he does not smell. Like the little old man in the beret Lambert also says,"Of course they torture people. They always have and they always will." He takes no pleasure in it. He is not a sadist. Three of his ribs are broken and he waits, lying there, to see whether it will get better or whether he will die of it. Long ago, he got himself invalided out of the army. Since then he has risked his life a couple of hundred times.

31

He is not an anarchist. He is reasonably in favour of a dictatorship and without knowing why he finds himself friends with a
great many men belonging to the right wing; they love his picturesqueness and they deeply appreciate his absence of thought.
Reasonably in favour of a dictatorship, but reasonably inclined
to blow up any dictator who inconveniences him. He has no
claim to logic. He is not fanatical. Lambert is a manufacturer,
and he dates from the time when manufacturers were also adven-
turers. That time will die with him. He knows it.

Lambert is quite good-natured, quite kindly-disposed. He loves
his family and he purrs with contentment when you wish him
many happy returns. He is a patriarch, and as such he is prepared
to feed his family. But his hand goes out automatically to grasp
the bosom of a daughter-in-law. He approves of fertility, but
with a masterful arm he brushes the children to one side. His wife
is thirty years younger than himself, and he employs remarkable
ingenuity in trying to deal with this state of affairs. He has accus-
tomed her to the bottle. For his part, of course, he drinks nothing
but milk. She cannot keep within bounds. "She will kill herself,"
says he, mildly. She is already seriously ill: she is extremely
nervous, and sometimes her memory goes. "She is mad," he states.
He makes the observation with an almost poetic smile upon his
beautiful old face. "I am the only one left who understands her."
He has found the perfect answer. She will die *at the same time as
himself.*

It remains to be seen whether she will let herself be eaten up.
If she were a philosopher she would be charmed to be immured
in this Altona. Georges Bataille, the poet, would have loved to be
this woman and to know the ecstasy of this *alienation.* That is not
the code of the noble beasts, which never refuse battle. With an
ever-renewed fury, Reine hurls herself into the fight for her sanity,
covers herself with blood, conquers for a moment and then falls
back; and she will never stop until she is dead.

Dialogue: Lambert (to the onlookers), "My poor Reine is very unwell this evening. She does not know what she is saying any more. Pay no attention." (She is there in an armchair just by him. There is no hypocritical whispering of the words: it is a fair blow, above the belt.) Reine comes up at once. She is not fifty yet, but she might seem to be—coarsened figure, beautiful hands, dark hair, dark, wide-ringed eyes, proud nose, and the unmerciful wrinkles furrowing her in every direction (she is not a woman who has been spared)—if it were not that her face is continually ablaze with the light of battle. (Literally ablaze, like that of Jahveh, God of Wrath, whose visage cannot be looked upon.)

"I don't know what I am saying?" she bursts out. "But it is you who have not stopped wearing me down and maddening me since this morning. You stopped me smoking at Mme X's, and when you introduced me you said 'My poor wife' and you have been making me drink, you . . . You . . . And it was you who did not know how old your son was when they asked you! It is you . . ."

She fights with the blind clumsy fury of womankind, darkly seeking for the divine moment when it will no longer be herself that is speaking but her fury, the eternal pythoness stammering out her onomatopoeic sounds which nobody understands, and which are the truth. He faces her in silence, concentrated, bracing his muscles, striking only blows that go home, winning in the end without pleasure, winning calmly. It is not he but a god that has defeated her. He is nothing and he is everything, making part of this god and being unaware of it.

Broken and no longer in command of herself, she also bows before this god. Tomorrow she will fight again. Today she feels neither resentment nor malice. They are united by a kind of peace. They are a pair. It is also what might be called a tolerably squalid scene.

A pretty subject, the state of nature. I have known it. Between the ages of fifteen and twenty-five I really do not suppose that I

33

ever thought, not as who should say *thought,* so much as once. And before then . . . childhood; and childhood does not count— it is a disease. Everybody thinks at twelve. The parents say, "She will get over it." And she does.

Lambert and his wife, yes. I see them under the most brilliant colours, their clashing swords, as beautiful as war . . . What is more, it is pleasant to be with them. They are not tedious. Even if they thought it necessary to turn upon you and rend, I still think you would like it, being aware of the imperative, over-riding need that alone could oblige them to act—no adulterated pleasure could do so. The great executioners are those who torture and kill without pleasure and without emotion—out of necessity. Pleasure is already remorse : remorse already pleasure. General X inflicts a moderate degree of torture upon himself and says, "You see? It's no worse than a visit to the dentist." He is wrong to justify himself, with his Colgate smile. You have to choose : inside Eden or outside it.

Inside, the generals who kill without any self-questioning, motor-car accidents, Lambert and his wife, and the Cora's shining children. Outside, the philosophers, the human generals who need reasons (Marxist or Western) to carry out their animal trade, the writers who try to find themselves in eroticism, the politicians who light the flame over the Unknown Warrior without dirtying their hands; and myself. Myself, in search of my theme and searched for by it; myself, wasting my time, I think, talking about

politics

Yet I had not meant to. Politics bore me, above all in novels. In the first place they bore me because of the dates, which I cannot remember. And then because it slows down the action. One grows interested in one character's career or in another's love-affairs, and then suddenly the wrong-headed author says to himself, "But I really must touch upon the great problems of our time." And he stops and deals us out a great dose of problem, whether we like it or not. You have to get it down before you are allowed to know whether X has inherited from his uncle and whether Y has gone to bed with the secretary. And you can see what it leads to when the whole book is made up of this sort of thing: the author turns into a minister!

Still, these passages concerned with immediate problems do have their use—they place a writer. *France-Observateur* esteems him; the *Figaro littéraire* does not pass him over unmentioned; the worthy *Lettres françaises* either accuses him or tears him to pieces; and no critic will ever confess that he finds all that stuff as dull as ditchwater and that the relationship between Shatov (*The Possessed*) and his wife, and the escapades of Prince Nikolai, are far more interesting than the precise shade of their opinions and the form of society that they want to impose upon Russia. And yet of all writers Dostoevsky is the one who makes the least possible division between his heroes' political ideas and their psychological and sentimental lives. Prince Nikolai does not launch into anarchism for reasons other than those for which he seduces Dasha. *Perhaps* S. is an anarchist out of love for mankind just as, out of love for mankind, he takes back his guilty wife. Though that is not certain.

But the others! How can you tell them apart amid the jumble of words that pours from their mouths, always the same jumble? You would say it was the same character talking, reflected in innumerable mirrors, like those advertisements in which the same thing is repeated an infinite number of times—a man talking politics begets another who talks politics who begets another . . . No, no; we must get back to love and to difficulties over money; and, at a pinch, to religious questions (because there is damnation, and that is always amusing). But love above all. You will say that my unbelievably frivolous female mind . . . and that you, a serious minded . . .

But let us speak honestly, and let us take a classic example: if you have read *War and Peace*, what do you remember of it? You remember Natasha. First of all Natasha, because you loved her. And then Pierre, who would have made such a perfect friend— if he had been yours, you would have loved him for his good-heartedness; you would have laughed up your sleeve, just a little, at his notions of reform, and you would have broken in upon his attempt at telling you about his Masonic lodge in order to boast about the charms of your fiancée. You may perhaps have thought Prince Andrei too hard on his wife; but that, you say, was only to be expected from a reactionary of his kind. Or else (according to your wife and your views on these matters) you will approve of his taste for *greatness*, and you will say that that is perfectly typical of women and their passion for bringing you down to earth . . . Is that not so, reader of Montherlant?

But I will bet that the eye of Montherlant himself wandered as he ran through those last pages about Napoleon, fate, great men —all those ideas, not entirely false, but dead, which Tolstoy bored everybody with for ten years in the provincial drawing-rooms, before taking to mending his own boots . . . And Martin du Gard! What a 'respectable body of work'! What a 'noble renunciation of the world'! (See the *Figaro littéraire*, always very generous in its admiration for detachment. But is it certain, absolutely certain, that some little dirty journalist with a winning leer and a scruffy overcoat, a pesterer of Brigitte Bardot and a collector of ill-natured gossip, would not nobly renounce the world if he were offered a château near the forest of Bellème? And that he would not set about providing us with an even longer *Eté 14*, for his greater glory and our greater boredom?)

Mind you, there are people who like that. There are others who like reading the papers. I am very fond of newspapers, too, par-ticularly those that have the same opinions as I have, like every-body else. But that is temptation; that is sin. So I read *Le Monde*, by way of self-denial, and (with a sigh) abandon the fascinating crimes of *France-Soir* and the indignant protests of *l'Express*. Not that these protests are unjustified. But indignation, to be pure, cannot take pleasure in itself. It must be a feeling of pain, and not one of pleasure. Reading a paper which shares one's own opinion, if one is reading not for the news but only for the echo of one's own anger, is a housemaid's delight : 'If only you could have seen his agonies, mam. The blood—he brought it up in buckets.'

For many people, politics is a pleasure of this kind. What would some of them do if there were no underprivileged Negroes, no persecuted Jews, no ill-used children, no prisons, no filthy slums? And our liking for the Jews, Negroes, children gives the exact measure of our hatred for those who use them as an excuse for mental masturbation. For that is what it is. And it is politics, too. Why does nobody ever say so? Politics is also the cuckold's inferiority complex, the shy person's alibi, the phallus of the impotent, the mistress of the man who lives alone. As such, it is interesting, and one can talk about it. But not as though it were an object. Not as though it were a distinct entity, a thing apart. Nothing is apart; nothing is shut off.

Do not let us close doors nor turn the living into statues : a statue is a very fine thing, but so is a bird too, don't you think?

statues

Lies, if you like. But the lie comes from both sides, from all sides. I was talking to Marcel (something of an Anglomaniac, very thin, a busy idler, would like to be thought imperturbable, but who cannot resist the pleasure of a witticism that with a well-calculated and picturesque explosion puts him out of character. The Resistance deprived him of both health and judgment. He spent three years in a concentration camp, and because of that he feels that he does not have to think any more at all for the rest of his days) about one of Valéry's poems and saying how I had liked it, when Marcel replied, "He was an anti-Dreyfusard." There for

37

him is the object, the thing apart, motionless for ever, stiff, seen in profile on a postcard; and he will never take the trouble to walk round it. Why should *he* stir himself? (Note: if you cross him in any way at all he makes his damaged lungs emit a long whistling sound. Sickness is also an excellent alibi.)

There are some people who say, "He's a communist. He's a negro. These Catholics . . . This kind of fellow . . ." These are very comforting classifications. Like that of the little old man in a beret some while back. They are not false. Nor are they true. There are old c———s, anti-Dreyfusards, communists, parish priests . . . But when this beret, this cassock, this red flag is *you*, oh most irreplaceable of mortals . . .

Alex, who professes cynicism and who loathes all admiration, holding it to be the mark of a gull, was talking to me one day about Garcia Lorca, and with a kind of delighted hatred he said, "Didn't you know that Lorca was a sodomite?" Still another sadly partial view. A view from behind, he would say, not being in the least afraid of the obvious. There is no sort of doubt that one of the most unpleasant kinds of falsehood is that of showing us nothing but the full-face view and the bust of great men.

The anti-Dreyfusard Valéry certainly explains Valéry the poet who became so quickly and so dubiously one of the nation's glories, so quickly and so dubiously a classic—explains, too, the words on the pediment of the Trocadéro. What can be more anti-Dreyfusard, more 'patriotic' (and one does not even have to call in Gallieni, who is just at hand)! Yet all the same, Valéry the poet also explains, renders human, and *to a certain degree* justifies the anti-Dreyfusard.

You forgive a short-sighted man for not being able to see; but he can easily make use of his short-sightedness to blunder into you and, blinking more than is quite right, to push his way into the bus in front of you. Which is to blame, the myopia, the presumption, or the bus? (In the same way you must have noticed—alibi-illness, alibi-old-age—the ferocity of white-haired old ladies with

medium-sized shopping-baskets who glide with a cat-like supple-
ness between you and the post-office counter, in spite of their
rheumatism. And look out for yourself if you are so bold as to
complain!)

And, fair enough, Lorca-the-victim was a sodomite; too much
jasmin in his poetry, too many stars, too many young toreros going green in the dawn in voluptuous death bear witness to that.
But for the café waiters and policemen to whom his vice (his
alleged vice, let us say, in order to make no judgment) forced him
to turn, do not all these olives and pure dawns, all this jasmin,
rip off the label—a label that is also thoroughly conventional?
Verde, que te quiero, verde . . . I love poetry. There was a time
when I did not like it, because of the way it was made use of. And
it is above all those who claim to be leaving it free who make use
of poetry.

Of those I have known, the one who spoke best about poetry
was a young man of 'good family' who worked on a paper that
used Catholicism, ye olde France, the good old ways and, oh, the
divine moderation of our race as a screen for defamation and
slander. You know the kind of thing. That too, by the way, is
only a label; and for the most part the minor employees were
earnest A.F. supporters, filled with solid worth and very fond of
good cooking. Take notice, indignant reader, that this label is
neither more nor less valid than that of the left-wing mental
masturbators a page before. I really must set everybody against
me; otherwise it would be no fun. And I will begin with my
friend

Luc

I am very fond of my friend Luc. He is an amusing shape, and
he looks as if he has just left off being a hobbledehoy. He is
extremely big, he has fair, fair hair (perhaps his paper insists upon
it, on racial grounds?) which stands on end, very gentle brown

eyes, a truly delightful smile and long bony hands which stroke the news, too, charming and caressing it so well that it takes on a polish, a lustre that is quite foreign to the *Agence France-Presse*. He comes to see us in the kindest way, my friend Luc; for we are not the kind of couple he ordinarily dines with. He is something of a snob; he crosses his long legs under ducal tables; dresses with a very careful carelessness, and likes to blend the washed mauve of a waistcoat with the green of a corduroy suit—almost something that you would go shooting in. (Let me inform evil minds that he is married and that he has children.) He is thirty-two and they say he has a fine future in journalism. I am not quite sure what they mean by that.

So he comes to see us out of friendship. He thinks us picturesque. We keep our children away from him—they are overfriendly—and he puts up with eating macaroni with the good grace of a tourist who has determined to bear all the drawbacks of the local colour. Yet he cannot bring himself to go so far as to endure our record-player. He likes only stereophonic machines: he is very fussy indeed, and he will not tolerate the slightest crackling. 'And I am positive that sometimes you lend your longplayers. What madness . . .' That is part of our picturesqueness too.

For him we form part of the 'little people' who read his paper and for whom he carries out his work of polishing the news. But he does not confine himself to the Nietzschean pleasure of feeling himself a superman among sub-friends. Generously and delicately he unfolds silks for us, spreads out engravings, offering us the finest, the most delectable things that his selective mind has chosen. He sets free the wings of poetry, and never has it flown so well, banking, flashing uselessly in a radiantly useless sky. *Verde, que te quiero . . . Et les belles écouteuses . . . Midi le juste . . . Le lait plat . . .* The free-flying bird has never seemed so free; never has the least of its sudden, studiedly awkward changes of direction been so foreseen, so deeply felt.

We are delighted: our heads are high in the air. But the bird is still flying, drunk *with being amidst the unknown foam and the skies*, when this man says, "And isn't it marvellous to be the truth for so many people? There is no one I admire as much as my patron—patron in the Latin sense of the word. A brute, of course—Caliban with Prospero's power. Suppose he took it into his head to run you down, you or somebody else—Françoise Sagan, for example. He doesn't like her. He is all for work-family-fatherland, like Pétain, you know; marvellous; he is perfecly sure of himself. 'Couldn't we say that she is a Jewess?' And if he said it, well it's extraordinary, but she *would* be a Jewess, you know!"

It is a poetic idea, indeed; one as shining as the bird that is flying, trilling, dashing forward in a flight that never leads on to an end . . . It is an idea that makes one want to shoot the bird. But it is not the bird's fault. It is only our dazzled eyes which do not see that something in the air which impedes its flight. It is only Luc's eyes which cannot see where this bird is going and which will not let him go anywhere. 'Like all the great butchers of history Tamerlane was a protector of the arts.' (Moravia.) One must still love poetry, nevertheless. For no more than the rest is poetry a thing

apart

I remember a publisher's luncheon party when I was in a high state of stupidity, blundering about among the forks, upsetting my glass, answering questions that were not addressed to me. Jean-Louis Barrault and Madeleine Renaud were there, and they encouraged me with their kindness, their sympathy; it was a genuine, sincere, warm sympathy, and I shall always feel grateful to them for it. Yet it was a sympathy that thought, and which was satisfied with thinking, "Ah, that is typical of a writer . . . The albatross 'whose giant wings prevent it from walking . . .' "

It is a notion that gives pleasure. It is the great delight of those who vilify the 'intellectuals'. Let the intellectuals write essays and the soldiers make war and the cows . . . By the way, who will look after the cows? With everybody leaving the land . . . There is another fine topical subject.

'Its giant wings prevent it from walking': yes. Very convenient for those who do walk and who take advantage of doing so to run everything according to their own ideas. "Ah, that is typical of a writer . . ." How many times has that not been said, wrapped in more or less of the honey of flattery, to writers who try to concern themselves with other things. "That is the intellectual way of looking at it," they say, too. Yet life itself is an intellectual way of looking at it. Each man to his own trade. Yet living is everyone's trade, after all. But we are not asked to do as much as that —just to take our places in the procession, in the costume of our trade, carrying the symbol of that trade and the name of the trade clearly written across the chest—changing it strictly prohibited, as on insurance cards.

Besides, it is pretty; it is picturesque. In the very agreeable folklore museum of Ghent there is a room full of these trade symbols, emblems that each guild carried before it in the processions. At the top of a staff there is a large figure representing the craftsman and his calling, carved in wood and painted. The weaver weaves emptiness; the cooper nails up emptiness; the goldsmith delicately prods dust. These emblems are little marvels of minuteness, and my old man in the beret is entranced by them. "Oh, the craftsmen of those times! They knew what work was then. Nowadays . . ." (The conversation generally branches off to the plumber who did not come on Thursday, or grows indignant on the subject of paid holidays.)

Beret admires the time-faded colours (it would be safe to bet that the beret of three centuries ago would have thought them dreadfully vulgar—even perhaps revolutionary?). Beret points out to his children or to the pupils he has brought to the museum on the half-holiday the perfection of the workmanship, the precision of the emblematic blacksmith's tools or those of the carpenter, and the exactitude of the tiny representation of the fifteenth-century town hall, complete to the last tile. There is only one thing that beret does not notice, and that is that the little leather-aproned smith, the little watchmaker with his magnifying-glass, the little joiner with his plane, have no faces. It is the same simplified head, a smooth egg-shape with a big nose stuck on it, a straight slit for the mouth and black spots for eyes, which has done for them all.

And you can easily imagine the little twentieth-century writer, made of chrome steel (we must move with the times) sitting at a café table which even has cigarette burns on it, holding a genuine contemporary ball-point pen and wearing sun-glasses, but topped by an oval on which even the hint of a nose and the trifling mouth have been done away with. Progress allows us this. And let the bird launch itself into the sky, cries Luc, in a splendid flight. And let him stay there, he adds, aside. Everyone agrees, even *France-Observateur*, which cries up the avant-garde writers and those dedicated to the absurd—even engaged painters, who show us the splendid workers, trade-union members, and the vile American soldier, all with the same egg-face, scarcely more than gone over once, in the case of the American, to put in the leer. Isn't that so, Fougeron?

Everyone agrees, I tell you.

I am very fond of ready-made phrases. Even when they are wrong they are full of meaning. "To play the game of the reactionaries," say some. "To play the game of the communists," say others. But have we not passed the age of playing? And what about this chess-board upon which we push forward our pawns, our civilizations? And isn't each one of us going to abolish the other's concentration-camps? Shall we never, never give up this game which excuses us from living, this chess which everyone can play on the little portable set he carries in his pocket? It happens with friends, businessmen, couples : at the least disagreement, out comes the chessboard. I shall certainly not play his game—and one advances a pawn. He is not obeying the rules; so much the worse for him—and one hurls oneself into the battle.

If couples reach this point, is it likely that nations will do any better? Faceless couples, faceless nations. "My wife is . . . After all I do have the right to . . ." "The Germans have presumed . . . It cannot be tolerated . . ." Certainly we have the right; and it cannot be tolerated : if you are playing, there are rules. But what if you are not playing? But if this woman, those Germans, that trade were you, the most irreplaceable of mortals, you would see a face on them, wouldn't you?

Everyone agrees. The caretaker and the journalist, to say nothing of the benign publisher. "Don't you bother with that, my dear. Work in peace, without any day-to-day worries. I will look after everything." They would undoubtedly look after your soul if they imagined that you had one (but they are too well-bred for that). Please note that I do not say this for my own; at least, not more for my own than the rest. Nor against

the businessmen

Basically, they are far more modest than a whole lot of shop-keepers flaunting their big Citroëns, and plenty of little unwashed teachers of Latin who shrewishly defend the spiritual values. Their indifferent digestions make them accessible to the pleasures of melancholy, which are not without their poetry. Their white telephones, through which voices from Chile or Mexico reach them, like the light of extinguished stars, make them aware of a sense of relativity. Their bodily unwieldiness, their awkwardness (have you seen a top executive who has dropped his fountain-pen, and whose secretary is not there, trying to pick it up from the place where it has fallen on the thick carpet, behind the impressive desk? And coming up, breathless, purple, rubbing his spectacles, and yet still patient, mild, and ready to repeat arguments that will convince neither you nor him, to the point of exhaustion?) their awkwardness, I say, teaches them patience, these gentle, bespectacled whales, these huge walruses half smothered in blubber, these pop-eyed seals stranded among the mahogany and the modern paintings.

Oh mature kinsmen of Barnabooth, oh cursed and disparaged race, blackguarded even in the *Figaro* serial, which you nevertheless read with meek acceptance, race with no touch of evil, without hatred except when you are brushed by the wing of fear (and even then you are sorry when you sack that trouble-maker, that head clerk; in private life you would certainly shake him by the hand, you, whom *Humanité* shows with an insult in your mouth at the same time as a cigar—which your weak heart will not allow you to smoke), race without illusions, which is far fonder of poets and of nature than the petit-bourgeois in his Nanteuil villa, race damned by the literary inquisition, I shall not add so much as a twig to the faggots they pile up at your feet. I shall only describe your eyes, eyes filled with the sad assurance that they are for ever proof against the fire.

a game

Behold me in the office of one of your kind—to cut it short, a cinema producer who wants me to do the dialogue for a film. He agrees with the idea, because for a few weeks he believes in the films of the new generation. I agree with the idea because I believe that this film will furnish my house in the country. I have told the director my price, he has passed it on and has sent agreement back to me. So it will be enough just to shake hands (for the human contact) and to sign. But no. The game must be played.

My producer arrives late. I (having foreseen this) a little later still. One point to me. He attacks at once. "Frankly, Mademoiselle

Mallet-Joris, I must confess to you [if the word *frankly* or *sincerely* is not uttered in the first ten minutes—or *let us speak openly*—then you are not in the presence of a genuine businessman, and he will certainly go bankrupt : take care], that I have never heard of you. When our director thought of you for this job—let us speak openly—I did not even know your name." I blush in spite of myself. One point to him.

He is aware of it, and he patiently goes on with what he has to say. Instead of turning to the dim, obscure Mallet, then, he might have called upon famous names, the guarantees of success and wealth—Jeanson, Audiard . . . But he is not one of those who always keep to the beaten track. *Audaces fortuna juvat!* (I bow, thanking him with a smile for this tribute to literature. Short truce. Two conscious, civilized Western minds greet one another.) Of course, he is running a great risk. With real talent he imitates the grimaces of the stars—"Who is this Mallet?"—and the terror of the distributors (a flock), who panic, crying, "Mallet? What on earth? You must be out of your mind."

But like all gifted people, he is swept away by his talent. He is astride a financial Pegasus that is carrying him far beyond the narrow bounds of mere probability. He is already ruining himself for me, and I am turning into the last straw that brings him to beggary together with his team; I am his costly whim, a creature he loads with diamonds, an Otéro. In another moment, unless I break in, overwhelmed by the weight of my guilt, he is going to tell me about his four children—me, whom he calls Mademoiselle, although my splendid six months' belly stares him in the face.

But the sparse remnants of fame that I still have in the bank give me a regal attitude. I understand him only too well. Of course, I have no wish to thrust myself upon him, when he has but to choose among such eminent specialists. Since this is the way things are, why, clearly . . . I fear that I must have misunderstood the suggestions of the slightly over-optimistic director; but I am very happy to have met him . . . I rise from my well-like chair, and with a gesture of amazement he sits me down again. One point to me. What? How could I think for a moment?

If he were acquainted with the classics his hair would rise upon his head, so horrified is he. That *he* should go back on his word! For it is his word, no less, that he has given the director. I do not know him. (It is my turn now.) His reputation in the business world . . . His honesty . . . There are sharks in this trade, but I am not dealing with one of them. He must tell me that whatever it costs him, his word is his bond—when he has said something, that is as good as a contract. (A stir of uneasiness within me. Is he going to ask me to do without a contract because of this outburst?) Would I like proof of it? What am I asking for this piece of work? Yes, what is my price? I am to speak boldly. Surprise makes me hesitate for a moment. And then there is that idiotic shame . . . A point to him.

Well (after a slight darkening of his brow: and do not miss the significant pause), well . . . all right. *He* does not argue: *he* does not quibble. He had not thought of giving more than half that to an author who is, after all, only just beginning in the cinema. But he likes me and he likes to trust in his intuition; besides, he feels that only a woman can provide the atmosphere that he wants for his film—in short, it's done, let's shake on it and say no more; he hopes that he has not done something stupid, he hopes that we shall be able to justify his trust in us, he hopes, he hopes . . .

With the same zeal that he used to tell me about his ruin, he now describes the realms of wealth we shall enter, the director and I, if we can make a good job of it. He sees me in a Jaguar, a cigarette between my lips, pushing my way through the crowd of my fans. "Cinema publicity is quite different from mere books, you know!" I wade in gold (other producers' gold); I buy a house in the country (I have one? Where? Normandy! But I shall have one in the south, at Saint-Tropez, at Antibes!) I do two scenarios a year, and my standard of living . . .

47

Confident that the deal is done, I take a cigarette and an air of supreme detachment. "Oh, I really don't feel like doing all that amount of film work, you know. This particular scenario quite charmed me because some of it reminds me of . . ." (This can be varied according to the producer; but one's author should not be too obscure. One can go as far as Stendhal. One can also assume a knowing, appreciative air. "It has something, an atmosphere . . ." This imprecision gives a highly professional touch.) "But a job of this kind every two or even three years would be plenty. Oh, plenty, I assure you."

"Why?" says he, out of countenance. (A point to me.) "Well, I am a writer, aren't I? That is my real work. And work on the cinema absorbs me entirely, absolutely entirely. I am not one of those writers who toss off this kind of job in three days on the pretext that it is not really literary work and that the public can be made to swallow anything at all. (Ah, you don't know me!) I do not despise film work, I think it as valid as any other kind of work, and he may be sure . . ."

"That's right—it will turn out well, won't it?" (At this point he is really touching.)

His enthusiasm is catching. Suddenly I too find myself hoping with immense ardour that it will turn out well. After all, it is pleasanter to turn out good work than bad. A feeling of kindness passes to and fro between us. The contract is brought in. It was quite ready. We sign it, pleased with one another.

But why, dear Lord? Why? And for whose benefit, these bullets fired on either side 'with no result', as they are in fashionable duels. Here is a worthy man, rather dumpy, both bodily and spiritually, with blue eyes and an open, ruddy face, not in the least wicked; a man who makes his money breed in a way no worse than anyone else. I should certainly do the same myself, if I had any money to make breed. So surely we can come to an understanding? He knows as well as I do that the fee I ask is not excessive. I know as well as he does that a writer is always delighted to do an easy and well-paid piece of work which will only take her a couple of months and which will furnish her house in the country. Well, then? Well then a hundred times over.

The game has to be played. Certain words have to be uttered. Between the publisher and the author, the producer and the scenario-writer, the seller and the buyer, the lover and the mistress, the politician and the elector, there has to be this ritual dance, like that of birds greatly in need of a mate or savages greatly in need of rain, this nuptial display, this war-dance, even if the marriage or the war has been decided or even finished long ago. And one joins the game in spite of oneself : one squares up. "After all, one cannot tolerate . . ." All fooled by the policy of grandeur. All incapable of taking the bull by the horns and getting out of the repetitive sequence.

All : myself included. For after all I could say to this man whom I rather like, and to my publisher, who is charming, and to the plumber who is fitting a shower for me ("It's not going to be easy, you know. What with these tiles and all, it's going to be an awkward job"), "Frankly, none of this is any use. Either we are of the same mind or we are not. Why try to wave imaginary advantages at me, since I accept the bargain because I see a genuine advantage in it—one that does not have to be waved at me at all. I am not taken in. Nor are you. What's the point of it, good God above? What's the point? Taking advantage, pretending that it is the other who is getting more out of it than you . . ." If only it were for making more money. But no : it is not even for that. It is to be the first to go through the door, to gather in that forced gratitude, that forced respect . . . "I shall not acknowledge him first." And they would rather give you a million which they do not owe you than a brass farthing which they do.

Capitalists, my dears, I can see you in a Negro film; you have reached Paradise in spite of everything, and you say to Saint Peter (whose paunch you think related to your own), "I trust you, of course. I will walk in with my eyes closed, without any argument.

I had expected something quite different, I tell you frankly—far better offers had been made to me; but I do not intend to argue. I will accept the package deal : I trust in my own intuition. I trust you. And I fancy that you will not mind being supported by people of my calibre, will you? That's right—you may count on me !" Capitalists, my dears, perhaps you will go to heaven after all?

heaven

"Heaven," said my little son Daniel, who is very thoughtful for his age, "is heaven the same for everyone? After all, not everyone likes the same things . . ." And with a shrewd air he added, "There is something wrong there."

It was that which was irking me a little in my recollection of my interview with the producer (a play that has been acted a hundred times). The sequence was perfect, the rules of the game simple, and the lines easy to remember. Yet there was something wrong. This game was not valid everywhere and with everyone. There were countless other games, apparently just as easy and just as permissible, but which one could not rely upon once and for all either. Not everyone likes the same things. One does not like the same things and one is not the same with everyone.

I had a vague notion of not being quite with it. These tunings, these very fine alterations according to the circumstances, the time and the clothes one was wearing did not suit me. Lack of adapta-bility, no doubt—a typically Germanic solemnity. Humourlessness and a liking for order—liking for order, above all, which begins with the right order in bills and extends to the order of the universe. And quotations come hurrying : "An injustice is better than a lack of order. Fine feelings do not produce good literature." People generally misquote this as *good feelings* : but they are wrong.

The one is as good as the other, and Tamerlane would have liked them both, no doubt. One can picture him too, in his Paradise, slashing off a head that rises above the others from time to time, between two poems and a sword-dance. And yet it is true that it is surprising that heaven should be supposed to be all of a kind, and that those mediaeval painters who imagined such a variety of torments in hell (you can pick whichever you like), should offer us no more than a stereotyped picture of heaven, with sexless angels and always the same flowery meads, never dreaming that one might have more hearty ideas than the pink and blue Paradise of Hieronymus Bosch. And yet on the other hand, little separate heavens, shut off like private rooms, for uncommitted poets and heroic cutters off of heads—no, there is something wrong there, too.

Lambert, Tamerlane, Luc, my producer, and truth : that does not amount to a theme for a novel. But still, perhaps it has a connexion with the novel that I want to write? With the choice of the theme, and the choice of this life that has obligingly stopped at my feet for a moment? Luc would say that it had not; so would Tamerlane. And Gide would be told; and Goethe would nod his wizened old head. No connexion. None at all. Perhaps. It would be very convenient if there were. Everything thoroughly in order, arranged and shut up. Fine feelings here, poems there, and the decapitated heads department at the far end : the Galeries Lafayette, a microcosm. Each in his own department, on earth as it is in heaven.

Yet it should be pointed out that even Gide, that edifying spirit (re-read Shakespeare for two hours this morning. Then worked on the sonata in B. Go over a little Greek this afternoon, if possible), did not set up a romantic anarchy in contrast to his Robert, the man of fine feelings, but two female figures who are not in the least disorderly. (Indeed, who could be more earnest, more virtuous, than Geneviève, the emancipated young woman! How seriously she goes about being a feminist! How solemnly she offers herself to Dr Marchand! Nothing could be less erotic, it must be admitted. How understandable is not the worthy doctor's hesitation! He is not tempted in the very least. It may be that Geneviève still belongs too much to the age of bad dressmakers, clumsy movements and pimples. How great a part does adolescent acne play in this noble refusal? But that is another story.)

What a genius Kipling was! Nobody has ever said anything better than this simple phrase: *That is another story*. All stories lead us on towards others, and wisdom lies in knowing where to stop. And yet who knows but that if we were to follow their wayward thread, these other stories would not lead us to the goal just as surely as the most rigid plan and the best-worked scheme; and whether all these stories might not form a single one, the only one?

This idea encourages me to choose a theme, a way of living. Perhaps after all it will have a connexion. We shall see. There are some people who set up this relationship so easily. Generally speaking I must admit that it infuriates me. Perhaps I do not know what it is that I want: but when "the great Christian writer" is interviewed and he declares that "he would not have written what he has written if he had not been a Christian," it amuses and at the same time it vexes me. How can he possibly know what he would have written if he had been someone else? So he is no surer of his belief but that he can so easily put himself in a state of unbelief? How it stirs one's curiosity! I should love to know what he has kept back. Murmuring perhaps as he did so, like Kipling, 'But that is another story . . .'

I confess that I should like to know this other story. Does his faith seem so far from all-embracing that the presence of certain objects makes him fear for its effulgence—and what objects are they? No, no; it is wrong of us to suspect him. He is only afraid of painting too attractive a picture of vice and of drawing people towards it. Of puffing the shop over the way, as it were. For him good literature is the literature that instills good feelings. Isn't that right? Perhaps deep down he is not very sure. If in doubt, abstain. And he abstains. From what? We shall never know.

And you? You are quite sure? You are in favour of free poetry, the free novel and free painting, like my friend Luc and Tamerlane? You are against fine feelings but not against good ones and you read Greek in the afternoon? Or are you with the Catholic writers? Do you hold back the brilliant description of vice just trembling on the end of your pen, thus heroically renouncing the Prix Goncourt, maybe: who knows? By the way, what makes you so sure that vice is so alluring?

But perhaps one day, with Mme de Beauvoir, you will dip your hand in a spring, and you will lose your faith. God, have You created springs, then, for the perdition of so amiable a woman as Mme de Beauvoir (I hope, at least, that she has bathed her fill since that day), as You created coach accidents to convert Pascal? At first sight this choice seems to me thoroughly unjust, for Mme de Beauvoir has a good head, has always done herself credit in her examinations and has gone for some splendid rambles, whereas Pascal prevented his entire household from eating meat prepared with a sauce, on the grounds that it was too pleasant. Nor is it clear what should prevent anyone from being converted by a spring, or losing his faith through an accident in a carriage. Considerations upon the innocence of springs and of books. I think that I could launch into that without regretting it.

Truth, falsehood, my life: all that is another story. A theme must be chosen.

Still, I am thirty—that age which seemed unattainable—I do have this house, this calling and these children, all grown-up attributes; these *views*, this life that is beginning to be a life that I have chosen . . . And even this book that I have not yet written, whose characters and theme I have not yet chosen, is it not already part and parcel of this life—in short, is it not already written, labelled, mummified, already 'my sixth book' or 'Françoise Mallet-Joris' fifth novel'; which is perfectly natural since I am a writer, and a writer turns out books, becomes a machine for writing books, and only the contrary state of affairs would be surprising. What I am asking, in short, is, "Is there a reason for writing this book?" And also, perhaps, "Is there a reason for living this life, my life, mine rather than another, or does it unwind itself automatically, mummified and labelled too, coming out of the machine like a long ribbon of paper marked with hieroglyphics?"

Is there any reason to write this book other than the doctor's and the tax-collector's bill, the patient delight in searching for words that suddenly match the image, the habit of these untroubled hours, this collecting, which dates from childhood; and the waiting publisher, the reader who 'must not be surfeited' by an over-abundant production nor yet 'discouraged' by too long a space between books . . . Is there any other reason for living than the presence of the person one loves, the fleeting grace of a child with a gap-toothed smile and a flat nose freckled with the passing heat of this Norman summer? But is there indeed a reason for searching for these reasons? Is it not enough that the machine should at last seem to be working without thumps?

Without thumps, but not without creaking. The creaks are Luc and Lucien, *Paris-Match*'s 'blond heads', and above all my own astonishment. Can that really be me? Is it really my theme, my novel? Can I really launch myself upon it without a second thought? There comes a moment when, after having groped about for a long while, I say *yes* to a theme. And I do not look back any more. One way or another, I shall reach port. Perhaps the moment has come to say *yes* to life?

Cocteau's lines come to my mind : *Riding on the roof of my lovely house Here I am in the middle years of my life* . . . I am not quite 'in the middle years of my life', but the situation of my attic and its wide view upon hedges, fields and hills, incites me to meditation; and as my dear mother would say, they are not without analogy with my moral, my mental situation as I cast my gaze upon the images, colours and perceptions that surround me, without yet settling, but without rejecting any detail either. Wait.

Meanwhile time is running, and as each recollection goes by it takes on the colour of my preoccupation, as if it were under a searchlight. I have only to see a face again, a tree, a house, to go back to balancing the object and the words, turning them in every direction, looking at them first from this side and then from that to see whether perhaps they may not contain a

theme

Record : just record. Wait for the sudden release, but *without trying to force it in any way at all*. First of all, record. Then analyse the elements. Arrange them in a hundred different ways. No : that is not it. Put them by. Later, perhaps . . .

But totally, *totally* unable to state why this particular theme and not that. Unable to state even why this way of handling it rather than another. If only I could manage to solve this little problem (with its comfortingly technical air), perhaps it would also help me to solve others. For example, why this life rather than another? Choice, hazard, fate? Let us pick a theme arbitrarily, by way of experiment, as one picks a book—to read. As one goes to call on someone : "I really must go and see X." Let us go and see

Alex

The flat is on the third floor. Let us walk in, darting Balzacian glances as we go. Let us go into the drawing-room-dining-room (they run into one another, to make the description easier) and sit in one of those excessively uncomfortable chairs made to look like scallop-shells : fluted seats, done over with silver paint. At the sight of them one feels instantly that this flat does not belong to an engaged, a committed man.

Two mantelpieces: on the one in the drawing-room, three bisque figures of 1900 women—quite charming, I must say. The dining-room mantelpiece has a fat German baroque angel made of vividly coloured china; and as far as I am concerned his fixed stare and his shiny smile make me feel postively ill. The master of the house likes to pick him up and point out the place where he is impaled so that he does not fall off.

The drawing-room has a piano, upon which Alex will presently sing you charming songs shot through with an inexplicable sadness. There is a little low table in the middle of the room, covered with deep red velvet fringed with gold: it is downright hideous. It is exactly like a conjuror's table, and you might expect to see doves, a bowl of goldfish or a bunch of artificial flowers. The fish-scale chairs are in a corner.

On the piano there is a stereoscope, and presently you will be able to admire its collection of views. There is a voyage to Japan in 1860, views of the Paris floods in 1910; and if Alex is particularly fond of you (or if he wants to be particularly embarrassing) you may contemplate a unique collection of 1900 nudes, lying on Moroccan rugs, crowning themselves with paper garlands, archly flogging themselves or even wearing a wreath of safety-pins round their breasts, with the points stuck in. There is also a trompe-l'oeil fresco of a hat-stand upon which a top-hat, a boa and some women's underclothes hang side by side.

That finishes the drawing-room and the dining-room, where, apart from the impaled angel, there are half a dozen ugly chairs and a commonplace table, none of which is worth speaking about. Now we must go along the corridor—rather mean and dark, like all the corridors in houses of that period. Moquette. And into the *little* drawing-room, next to the bed-room, where one has coffee. Red velvet still. Tortuous knick-knacks on the mantelpiece. Record-player: it works indifferently, but it is concealed in quite a fine Renaissance chest, painted all over. A tranquil, shut-in atmosphere. A little piece of furniture covered with papers and magazines. A really splendid Louis XIII table. An armchair of the same period tarted up and spoilt by a lectern which can be turned into a desk. Water colours of theatre sets. Here comes the coffee.

Alex pours it out with great goodwill. The frivolous shortening of his name suits him admirably: he is slim and light in spite of being nearly fifty; his intelligent face is covered with a network of little wrinkles; sensitive hands; gentle, uneasy eyes; smile ironic and sharply-defined: hiatus. He speaks with animation—formerly one would have said with wit. And yet after a moment you are surprised. Suppose you have been talking about a rather vulgar musical, a hit: "It must be good, since it is a success," says Alex, his face suddenly going hard.

He cannot bear that anyone should think he had been affected by the failure, the relative failure, of the two musicals that he wrote at an earlier period, before devoting himself to cinema music. And he starts off on an almost Nietzschean theory about successful plays. If you do not succeed in the theatre it is because you do not deserve to succeed. Good music always gives pleasure. People always like good music: they always read a good book. A man with something in him always succeeds. His gentle, tired face takes on a fanatical harshness. Pitilessly he proceeds with his own execution: "A moderate success means a moderate talent. One must be clear-minded."

That is his slogan, just as it is that of the mackintoshed girls at the university who think themselves 'modern'. Uncommonly naïve, at his age. One must be clear-minded. It was Alex who said to me, with something like hatred in his voice, "And your Garcia Lorca was only a sodomite, after all." And yet who, on the face of it, could be more easy-going about the vices of others? Who more urbane, who more Parisian, more devoted to first-nights and cocktail-parties where every kind of person is to be found; who more surrounded by ambiguous actors, accommodating singers, idle wealthy men in search of amusement? Who so

57

keen on making game of any inquiry, any policy, any new thing if it is serious, all religion if it is not social religion, all virtue?

All virtue . . . I am still looking for a man who does not make a virtue of having none. The simple, natural man lyrically invoked by the surrealists, sadly admired by the philosophers, the man the reactionaries and the progressives pretend to be when they are badly in need of a programme (oh, their use of the adjective *healthy*!), that 'force of nature' women dream about, tired with the effort of building up Don Juans for centuries past, that man with neither complexes nor scruples whom the left-winger sometimes dreams of when he forgets politics for a moment, that man whom the dear poet Georges Bataille tried so hard to resemble (with no success, thank God)—why should he, this force of nature (in so many ways identical with the robust grocer on the corner of the street), loathe virtue? Nature does not loathe virtue: it is unaware of its existence. And here I am back at innocence. Alex is a great way from it. Alex, who claims to be an eighteenth-century being, a man of the *ancien régime* (the eighteenth century of pastorals, mechanical toys, minuets and Crébillon: not that of Diderot), nevertheless has this veneration for the 'force of nature' which is peculiar to our time, our century that is starving for Eden, sick with longing for the verdant Paradise.

Alex hardly reads anything at all. To him it would seem pretentious. Yet for a long while he was quite enchanted by a book on Sarah Bernhardt, a kind of Sarah Bernhardt in bedroom slippers, with its revelations, and all their dubious bedroom smell. The little scandalous personal sidelights of history are his delight. The idea that Michelet, as well as being the great historian everyone knows about, was also wildly over-sexed, has an inexplicable charm for him. If someone speaks to him of the beauty of one of Racine's tragedies, he triumphantly replies, "Racine loved young men, and he was implicated in the Affair of the Poisons. Garcia Lorca . . ."

His pet subject is Madame de Sévigné. Oh, Madame de

Sévigné! Maternal love, eh? Forgive my laughter. He seeks out the interpolations, the changes and the suppressions in the famous letters with the zeal of a scholar or of an informer. If only he could find the proof of some illicit passion between the mother and daughter he would have the feeling that he had triumphed. Triumphed over what, tender-hearted Alex? Over yourself? The love of truth, as Jean Cassou points out so well, is a murky passion . . . But here is it really a question of the truth, or only of *a* truth?

Here we are, Alex's friends: we have gathered for coffee. Friends?

A delightful sodomite (so what about Garcia Lorca, then? But Alex *loves* surrounding himself with homosexuals. In exactly the same proportion that their perversion seems to him to be a taint and so to contribute to his general debunking attitude); a little actress (before making her his mistress he made sure that she had no future); an older actress who goes with him to the flea market and to certain functions where you leave your clothes (all of them) in the cloak-room; an 'old friend', a clerk in a commercial firm; an astonishingly vulgar journalist with black curls who calls him *toi*, slaps him on the back and, like a simpleton, thinks himself his best friend, never working out the meaning of the reptilian glance that rests upon him, nor the questionable pleasure that Alex feels in appearing to say as he introduces him, "Yes, indeed. These are the sort of people I like to go about with. At all events, they are undisguised. They are swine in the state of nature. Like you: like me. If you find them disagreeable, that is only your hypocrisy."

And it is not that he is really so revolting, the harmless journalist with the Greek hair-do, who works on a vaguely pornographic paper; and I find it quite touching to see him sit down at the piano to sing some filthy song, immersed in the charm of his well-rounded southern voice, as if he were Tino Rossi. Nor is she really so stupid, the little actress who is only doing

59

what she can to get to the top, naturally, and for whom Alex is
primarily a means of having auditions, being properly dressed,
being seen at the Elysée-Club and having her hair done at
Garland's; but she would like to mingle a little feeling with all
this, the very small, cut-price fondness that she does possess, that
corner of Woolworth's which asks no more than to be allowed to
flower: for her, since she is not 'clear-minded' it would make it all
a little easier to put up with.

And the friend of the flea market and the curious parties is
not so utterly devoid of virtue, either; faced with age she is brave,
and faced with half-success (the kind that is so charmingly called
a *succès d'estime,* so true is it that esteem or respect has never fed
anyone) she is brave. Brave, faced with the repugnance that 'the
burning pleasure unshaded by remorse' brings to those who are
devoid of scruples. And that old friend in front of whom you can
strip without the slightest shame (he has not succeeded, you see),
and who is perhaps wise enough to make no judgment upon
you—he is not so commonplace, either. And what of Alex?

Is he as complicated as he seems? As uncomplicated as he
would like to be (the source of your charm, Poujade!)? Is he
simply this Clouet drawing of the face of an unhappy man?

I am not sure that Alex would make a good character. After
all, you have to be able to lay a character out flat, to spread it: it
is a picture rather than a piece of sculpture. A certain degree of
complexity is not a bad thing; but it must lead somewhere. The
reader must be able to say, "Oh, that's it! That's why he was
like that. I see now." Obviously, this is a concept of the novel
that still borders on the detective story, upon mechanics, even
upon pottering about with tools.

The amount of indirect damage that Freud, the old River-God,
has managed to inflict upon traditional psychology is quite
astonishing. Balzac's psychology, the scrupulous description of the
soul in its outward manifestations, bringing old Pons down to
the status of an object and raising Grandet's wealth to that of a

character, that descriptive psychology is fundamentally very close to the New Novel and its abstractions, just as the unadulterated picturesque is very close to the absurd— *Marienbad,* that triumph of the baroque, is an excellent illustration of this coming together. A theory to uphold in a 'scintillating' essay. *Balzac the New Novel writer!* The salt-pans of Le Croisic (in the splendid *Béatrix,* beloved by so many poets, Gracq and Breton among them) possess that inimitable mystery of things; the fascination of Béatrix (that mummy) for the young and handsome Caliste is never *explained.*

What a delightful parallel one might draw between Balzac and Pinget, for example! Even if one went no further than that love for bric-à-brac . . . We are far from the Freudian crossword puzzle—a complex in six letters, and we have the clue. Detective-story: nothing more. Oedipus is the murderer (and the tell-tale tortuous demeanour of the psychoanalysts! Informers, simultaneously the executioners and the accomplices of those they pursue). All this is perfectly simple—merely a question of cogs and wheels.

Alex might be

Alex might be a Balzac character, a 'given' character; in short, one scarcely removed from the object-character that we hear so much about. But the reader wants an explanation. It is no good telling him that to understand is not necessarily the same as to explain. He wants a character in the dock who may be acquitted or who may be found guilty; and he wants to be the jury. *A letter to my Judge* is as much a formula for the novel as a title. A good machine: a machine that works well. Why not? There are others. There are also good novels. Alex could be described. Alex could be judged, used as the chief character in a well-contrived adventure, called upon to bear witness to a ready-made world. But how to make the choice? And can I choose? Let us imagine it for a moment . . .

Subject for essay: describe a composer of cinema music,

unmarried, well-to-do, over forty. His various aspects. End by giving your opinion.

Such a clear, comforting sort of question. I loved that kind of work at school, centuries ago, the other day. Why has the work of writing not remained so uncomplicated, with the new pen one has chosen and the fine white paper upon which one is about to draw up a scrupulously careful plan . . . But let us get on with our description . . .

First aspect: *the stock* marquis *role in the theatre.* He calls to mind the eighteenth century and its delightful frivolity. Prefers the pretty to the beautiful, the bizarre to the true, and above all he hoots down whatever is earnest. Full of paradox and charm, bears with all vices, is open to all temptations so long as they lead to nothing. Neither a politician nor a mystic; disillusioned with all that, and with love, which he chooses to look upon as no more than playful manoeuvres—a kind of sham war. A touch of stylish sadism. A Vailland character. A character for Vailland.

Second aspect: *'Poujadist'*. His obvious love and respect for success. And then his outspoken respect for *social* (never for moral) values. The left wing seems to him blameable both because it makes moral claims (first aspect), and because it is not in power (second aspect). He is fond of talking about *efficiency*, and he says "Politics and morals are two different things." He quotes Goethe, "I prefer an injustice to a want of order." And in spite of the fact that his digestion is delicate, his fear of seeming to be a worn-out intellectual sometimes makes him pretend to admire the opaque stupidity of some gormandizing, swilling teller of dirty stories. He never parks his car where it might be a nuisance to anyone else. He sends his donation to a religious charity that looks after waifs. The full bourgeois equipment: perfectly ready to go straight into the *Humanité* serial. Let us leave it to him.

Third aspect: his deviousness. He is surrounded by odd creatures, and he takes pleasure in the fact. He spies on his mistresses and takes a kind of delight in proving to them that they do not love him. When he knows that he has been deceived (and robbed, on one occasion), he performs a cat and mouse act, tormenting both the guilty woman and himself. He loves anything that lowers, that diminishes—take the case of Madame de Sévigné. He has an inexhaustible fund of stories about the vices of others. With fanatical zeal he detects hypocrisy and credulity everywhere. Often he is right. It wounds him, but he is no longer consciously aware of his suffering. M. Mauriac has but to take up his pen. The work has already been done and nothing remains but to bring the gleam of salvation into the darkness. And if one looks carefully, may it not be found in that flowing music, as limpid as an imprisoned spring?

hells

As far as I am concerned, I should quite like to use him to draw that picture of a person insane enough to want to be damned. Damned without any cauldrons or pitch-fork devils, of course. Like my little boy, I am quite ready to believe that 'hell is not the same for everybody'. And when I speak of damnation, as I see it, it is quite certainly not bound up with one form of political opinion or one way of making love. I am talking of that damnation which everyone can understand, that damnation which consists of an intelligent man becoming voluntarily stupid, of a sensitive man in his turn becoming voluntarily hard, of a man who has been hurt becoming the one who in his turn inflicts pain, of a proud man humiliating himself to prevent himself being humiliated.

I am talking about that kind of damnation in which a cultivated man reaches the point of reading the illustrated magazines and the pitiful blood-and-thunder that is designed to charm innocent servants and thick-witted juvenile delinquents. I am talking about that damnation in which a man capable of love goes down from woman to woman to the very bottom (or what he supposes the very bottom; for there is no being so low as not to deserve love). I am speaking of that damnation which consists of voluntarily choosing, out of pride and fear, the easiest, the most unjust and the narrowest.

The innocent maid-servant, did you say? The innocent beer-drinker? The innocent teddy-boy? Yes, I did; and I confess that by this long detour I have come back again to heaven and hell. Some saint—I forget which—said, "There can be sin even in drinking a glass of water." And my innocents burst out laughing. Oh, these Christians' love for suffering! Their guilt-complex! A glass of water! Really! Drink on, drink on, my dears. Gulp it down: never stint yourselves, you will never succeed in putting a sin in it; and perhaps that may be so much the worse for you.

It is a fine thing to see an innocent man: he drinks, he lies about, he kills, rapes, tortures; and he never leaves his wild and lovely Eden. "He who does not belong to the law shall not be judged according to the law." That is just what I was saying: Eden is full of cops; the virgin forest with its beautiful poisonous flowers (the flowers are guiltless too), the quiet, all-engulfing forest which the Douanier Rousseau painted so well, is full of wild beasts with beautiful eyes, of heavenly blue serpents, of gentle does that yield themselves to martyrdom. And the red flesh under the claws, the quivering flesh that still remembers life, is more innocent than that glass of water at the sinner's lips, than that magazine in the hands of my intelligent *character*.

And between ourselves, this entirely excuses the glass of water and the magazine, as objects; rape and murder, as objects; and sin, as an object; and the interdict pronounced by our little Christian novelists on this poor innocent flesh, this poor guiltless lechery, which haunts their longing thoughts just as the glass of water would haunt them if only they had been told often enough that sin dwelt therein. (And I hope to God that someone has told them! I am sorry for the wives of the young Christian novelists.)

Each man has his own sin, except perhaps Tamerlane, that

innocent who made more than a hundred thousand heads roll at Delhi. Neither Luc nor Alex have caused a single head to leave its neck (it must be admitted that they have never had the chance of doing so); but I prefer Tamerlane. Like my little boy, that positive fount of wisdom, who, on reading *Taras Bulba*, trembled, wondered and said, "Taras Bulba has burnt down seventeen villages; now it is him that has got burnt. It is not right; but it is splendid." Yes, it is splendid, as a blazing house is splendid. I am not against blazing houses myself. It is the false neon blazes that I dislike.

Now this detour has brought me back to truth and falsity, and to myself. To those questions that come into my mind because I have seen myself reflected in a human mirror, as a character: yes, as a character—why not?

But is not that what I wanted, when I was a child? To be someone? And why call it all into question? Only ten years ago—or not even ten, perhaps seven or eight years ago—no such question would ever have entered my head. As I have said, I did not think. That may seem strange, and I will be blamed for having altered. But what can I do about it? Come, I see that I really shall have to talk about myself.

At fifteen, a lover: not taken at all shamelessly (I underline this —it is not a question of a railway-bookstall novel) but through the natural call of my body and my heart. It would have been wonderful if I had taken a lover as ingenuous as myself; we should have lived through a few months of eternity amid the great untroubled leaves of the jungle, under the benign gaze of the tame lions, friends of the Adam and Eve one knows from pictures. Even the serpent would have found nothing to carp at.

I chose badly; or rather I did not choose at all. The only man that circumstances allowed me to meet, whose means opened the paradise of furnished rooms to him, and whose nature was such that I could love him, was a thinking being. He put me through a course of lectures upon the freedom of the individual, upon

65

clear-mindedness (that again, God help us!) upon emancipation from bourgeois conventions . . . I absorbed only enough of all this to deceive him a little earlier and with a little less spontaneity than I should have done if he had said nothing. If he had preached virtue, perhaps I would have kept to the narrow path for a few years, to please him. As I have said, I had no principles.

At that time my parents interfered with me, and so I loathed them, to the infinite delight of this complicated man. And how virtuous an indignation (virtuous is the only possible word) did he not feel when I once more began to love them with a simple, animal fondness as soon as I was out of their control and as soon as they no longer hindered me! In the same way, once their natural, if not legitimate, anger was over, they came back to the same sort of kindness for me and for the child of my wanderings.

We never quarrelled about anything any more. In fact, we never thought about it again. We remained in that forest in which once you are no longer hungry you no longer kill anyone. We were on the same side. I did not disapprove of the man I loved: the idea of judging anyone at all was entirely foreign to me: I just stopped loving him. While I was with him I had come by a certain style that made it possible for me to write a book—the first. I had always written. I wrote harder than ever when it became clear to me that writing would sometimes allow me to make money.

I went on not thinking. It is a very pleasant state. Unhappily there is no way of returning to it. Nostalgia for the verdant paradise cannot be avoided: but making one's way back towards it can only result in turning everything different that is coming into existence into a pillar of salt. It is quite obvious that children are more beautiful than adults. Out of any ten children, seven or eight are delightful; whereas out of ten men . . . But adults are more beautiful than the senile. Do not let us follow the way of the world, the stultifying world which, having been so unwary as to turn round, finds itself frozen where it stands into a statue (a statue in the shape of a general).

It is a privilege to reach the age of twenty-two in a state of innocence. The man I no longer loved (the feeling was mutual, it must be added : he was aware of the proprieties) went on keeping me for several years. We continued to be friends. His generosity seemed to me quite natural; but the reverse would not have surprised me, either. I went on writing. My son grew, and I was fond of him. My people had started sending me letters again and seeing me, and I was fond of them. I did not think myself obliged to make love, except every now and then, and by chance. I did not live a wild sort of a life: I went home early because I was sleepy; I worked because I liked working; I made love when I wanted to, not very often; and I spent little because I had little to spend. I lived a free life. That means that when I talk about Eden, I am talking about something I know. But once I had become aware of it and had named it, I had already left it.

When I grew acquainted with Truth
I thought she was a friend :
By the time I had understood her and known her
I no longer had any liking left . . .
But was Eden the truth?

rooms

There is always a certain want of shame in talking of oneself, and I should like to avoid it. I do not like the confessional tone. This passage in Balzac comes to my mind : 'On her walls Béatrix had watercolours of the various bedrooms in which she had stayed during her travels, which gave the measure of a really outstanding effrontery.' I do not particularly want to stand out in that way. Besides, I have not got such a good memory as all that; and I am not clever at watercolours. Bedrooms : no, I shall avoid the subject as far as possible. Not completely, however; for on so simple a subject I should not like to lack simplicity. But there are so many other rooms that are far more shut away than a bedroom! In the first place, all the rooms in which one writes. At any rate that seems to me to be the case. I brought back the discoveries that I had made outside to that 'room of one's own', I gazed at them, I sorted them, and I was amazed, it seemed to me, at possessing so many things.

When I lived at Neuilly one of my chief delights was to go out after dinner (a dream of childhood at last fulfilled) and sit on a bench on the avenue de la Grande Armée in the darkness, watching the cars go by with their headlights on, streaming towards the Arc de Triomphe. That bench reminded me of another, which was in a park near my parents' house, where I used to go and sit in the same way, stealing a few moments from the too-rigid programme of the day.

I was a very regimented child, a prisoner in a big house that ran like clockwork, and for me freedom meant solitude. My first discovery. When I began to have private lessons, it was a vivid pleasure not to go home at set hours but to stroll about the streets a little, to have a cup of coffee alone somewhere, to feel myself sheltered in the crowd, unknown, invisible. Alone: protected. A room, already. Presently there was the pleasure of losing myself in a book. Reading, morning, noon and night, in any place at all, became a positive disease. My parents had a very large, very varied library, and I read everything it provided. I read a great deal, and very badly: how many books I have rediscovered since then! Reading: this was another way of being alone, being hidden; and so was writing. But writing also meant employing things, and arranging them.

Yes, it was in writing those little poems, which must have been most artlessly lyrical (I have never re-read them) that I knew my first deep, strong feeling of joy. The violence, the sadness, the joy that I felt were not passing shades of feeling, idle moments, reflexions; they were the bricks, set one upon another, which were to make a building; they were the separate pieces all coming together to form a house. What a sudden feeling of peace to think that nothing was useless in that short imprisoned adolescence. I was athirst for solidity, usefulness, eternity, without either knowing it or shaping the thought in my mind. The need to write was at once turned into a calling. From enthusiasm I passed quickly to inquiry; at the end of each day I brought back my loot of words and impressions, and I botanized them with care. The work gave me peace for seven or eight years. Instinctively I loved order. Only I thought it could be confined to a single area. I cheated; but so unthinkingly. I was a happy animal.

After my first novel I discovered the pleasure of making money. I liked it immensely. It completed my liberation. At last I had my being unhampered by any tie. I was living with reference to society, if you like. I went to the restaurant alone, carrying a paper and feeling intensely important. My life also was taking shape, I thought. It did not appear to me that I had friends, although I sometimes went out with a group of people I knew; but seldom. For me my son was a little pet animal, physically agreeable. And my parents, a somewhat distant warmth, like a good fire in a room—that warmth that I knew I could go to if I needed, but which was formless and without life of its own. The man who provided me with a home had become that, too. A good fire, to which I was fairly grateful since nothing obliged me to warm myself.

I liked reading, walking, eating, sleeping; going to the cinema sometimes; sometimes, in the vaguest way, feeling that I was cared for, that I was loved: but not too much. I knew nothing about art: painting left me unmoved, though with sometimes a slight feeling of pleasure; it was said that I liked music, because it soothed me; I had no opinions on either political or moral questions, nothing more than the feeling that all those things were very dreary.

I worked steadily, and I took pleasure in working. Now and

69

then some image would suddenly come to me and I would put it on one side to use it or to think about it one day that never came. On one occasion I saw a landscape, and I saw that it was beautiful; and that astonished me, for the countryside seemed to me to be another of those things that were very dreary. Another time, at Venice, I really *saw* a picture (a Tintoretto), and I felt the same astonished delight. I did not know that one could really take pleasure in beauty. It had seemed to me an affectation, the kind of thing one said. Until then I had only liked *nourishment*. I must have been easy to get on with, I think.

And here is another room : one day, in a hotel room with a wallpaper of silver hydrangeas on a dark blue background, a commonplace man asked me if I loved him and the question made me sad, although I could not tell why.

It must have been fine outside. The windows, with their heavy curtains greasy with dust, gave on to a cool, shaded courtyard, as echoing as a well. At the end of this courtyard a man was clearing his throat; he cleared it carefully, for a long time, spat, and then began singing quietly. The afternoon had that peculiar resonance which a very blue sky seems to give to Paris when it is rather empty. I was lying there, stretched out in the silence, with my body calm and relaxed and the pleasant smell of a cigarette in my mouth, and I *saw* that afternoon (just as for the first time I had *seen* a painting); I saw it purposeless, not devoid of charm, but unrelated to anything, floating like a flower on the water; and that question, purposeless too, floated like a water-lily with no roots. I was there : I might equally well not have been there. A little more sun or a little less, one word rather than another, a look, a smell . . . I was floating in the sunlight, useless, unrelated to anything. It was the foam of myself that was letting the wind waft it here and there like this over the black water, and the sun decided whether it should land here or there, and I, on the shore . . .

I went no further with this thought, which scarcely took full

shape in my almost pleasurable uneasiness. I had only something
of a wish to go away, that's all. The wind had changed. Later I
broke with this man. It was one evening at about seven o'clock,
in the Champs-Elysées. We were walking, and as we walked the
lights went on all along the dark gardens. I was surprised to see
that he was hurt: no doubt he did feel a kind of liking for me,
after all. Why had he not told me? We might equally well not
have parted. Perhaps my weariness came as much from the heat
of that spring as from his being there? Perhaps we could have
swum against the tide that was separating us with its pitiless softness? I did not put that thought into shape, for want of words to
do it with.

I had a little money. I made up my mind to go on

a journey

To leave all these old people behind me. Parents, or the memory
of parents. Men and their male conversation. Work. The beginning of a feeling of something wrong; a great desire for the
gratuitous, and for emptiness.

We set off on foot with rucksacks, hitch-hiking in fine weather:
the beginning of a sentimental novel, suitable for young people. I
crammed myself with it. And with the landscapes, the suddenly
uncovered landscapes, and the fresh air, and the unexpectedness
of the places where we stopped, and with this young man, whom
I thought so good-looking. We went as far as Spain. Political,
moral or artistic questions never came into it for a moment. But
I could breathe properly. And he was very proud of having a
'mistress'.

We were children hiding in a garden being called by the grown-
ups and amusing themselves by not answering. We watched the
evening darken, sitting at café tables in little squares, with innocu-
ous drinks in front of us, and we felt ourselves far freer than so
many penned up boys and girls. Accomplices, too. Between us we

already had something to hide, something that was not to be seen. So many beds with brass knobs, so many crocheted counterpanes, so many chintz curtains, and the sun on our brown legs . . . So many towns with museums that we did not see.

But there is no doubt that we stroked every cat in Toledo, laughed at every smart young Spaniard, with his perfectly polished co-respondent shoes and his supercilious way of eating an olive. And we certainly wandered into every bar in Madrid, that burning, chromium-plated city, a true woman in its heat and its ugliness. I fell in love with a Murillo in the Prado. No excuse. Not a Velasquez nor a Ribera nor anything that might in some way be justified: a Murillo. Too much paella: we decided to have upset livers; we slept in the afternoon, with the slatted shutters thowing hearts on to the tiled floor of the bedroom.

We read out-of-date papers. The call of the blind men selling lottery tickets to be drawn today—*Para hoy! Para hoy!*—was like the sound of crickets, a shrill emanation of the heat. We talked about ourselves, inventing some really charming things, playing games and cheating a little. And always cool water to drink, put discreetly at the door by the *criada*—and just so that we should not be disappointed she was beautiful, too. And poetry in both our mouths . . .

It was still fine when we got back to Paris. If we had known, we should have understood that it was a perfect day for a break. We did not know. We had scarcely made our way out of the womb of innocence and our eyes were still stuck shut like those of undried kittens. We cheated, but with no malice aforethought. We had not yet reached the stage of those determined primitives who know the rules of hygiene and who remorselessly apply them. We said we would go on seeing one another. A second love spoilt. And yet that is not an excessive rate, when you think how these things go in Paris. We became a couple. It could only end in tears.

Rooms. My love was in this, my work was in that. No communication between the two. The doors closed carefully behind

one. At the same time that I was living without rules and in that
preserved yet threatened innocence, I was choosing a theme, as
I am choosing one today.

A theme that was to hold me prisoner for two years on end. A
theme that was to oblige me to overcome doubts and headaches,
anxiety and pains in my back, to force me to get up early and
refuse to go to the cinema in the evening or for a walk in the
morning, for two years—for two years is my rhythm. Doubts
which came before the decision : I might be mistaken.

This image that fascinated me, this character I found so attractive, this approach that seemed the right one for my more far-
reaching efforts—perhaps they would not give the ring I wanted.
Perhaps after all another theme, a less attractive theme on the face
of it, might really answer my purpose better? Might be more
clearly understood? Or even : might perhaps bring in more
money?

I do not blush for these motives; for this desire to communicate,
to enter into relations with the world, even on a material basis, is
part of my nature, and it has its importance. Unlike many people,
I am glad that this trade of writing should *also* be a trade. The
'also' has its importance.

But in the end I make up my mind today as I did then. Put
doubts to one side and, once everything is as well weighed as I
can manage, leave all further ponderings from this moment on.
For two years. Sit down every morning in front of this theme as if
it were the only one. Work your way down into it; lop off the
redundancies that slip in . . . (if one took as much care with love
as one does with work, love would be much the better for it, no
doubt). If the work is a back-breaking grind and the result dull
and disappointing, I still know that the next day will see me at
the task, until that day of grace when everything will come alive
and seem always to have been in existence : whereas in our relations with our fellows a single word, one rather dismal, unhappy
day, will call everything into question. This patience, forcibly

73

taught by the work of every day and thus unknowingly driving a mine under the afternoon's happy innocence—perhaps my theme lies there, the theme that I should like to take up now?

But when I came back from that journey I was hesitating between two subjects: I deliberated, deliberated again, and made these

notes

A stupid but uncomplicated girl brought into a more 'civilized' milieu: *involuntarily* coming to mean something, *unknowingly* setting up eddies about her which soon prove fatal to her. Carried along by the logic of her actions (though she does not understand it) to stimulate and to show up the falsehood that surrounds her.

Or else a man writing his private diary, falsifying his role as he goes and lured on thereby to make decisions that will be hurtful to himself . . . Or some sort of public opinion comparing the man who writes and the man who lives and obliging him to bring the two into line, not out of any love for truth, but so as not to see his own lie so blatant—acted out, as it were, by this blundering fellow on the stage. The magic role of the *acted play*. Hamlet. In this case the magic works in the contrary direction to that foreseen. Part played by private diaries: picking out the truth, disguising it. Go into this thoroughly.

These notes were laboriously written out, together with many others, in my private diary: considering how I was placed at that time, are they not in the highest degree

comic ?

That is how they look to me. Is it possible that I having sat pencil in hand, almost every day since I first learnt to write, completely taken up with searching out the meaning of words, with reflecting upon them, with being patient in the midst of impatience, hoping

74

in hopelessness—is it possible that I could so sincerely have thought that once I put my pencil down I could escape from that reflexion, that inquiry! Is it possible that I should miraculously succeed in doing so for years on end, and with a splendid blindness remain ignorant of the meaning and almost of the existence of those little gnawing uneasinesses which were trying to make their way into the light (and then suddenly opening my eyes and discovering that I was alive and being amazed by it)!

What can be funnier, after all, than becoming in one's turn a character in this everlasting tale of a self-confrontation, whatever it may be, when one has written on all these themes and used all these terms—'relationships', 'revelation' and so on a hundred times—and as if they were harmless!

It is too much altogether: slap-stick farce. And yet how ingenuously candid I was! And how could I tell that that commonplace instant between longing and dread, when you say "Shall we see one another again?"—that already that instant was no longer entirely pure: or was it not pure yet?

I should like to leave this subject alone; and yet I still have to tell how I spoilt my first love. Right away I must tell you, by way of reassurance, that I have only had three; and since the third has been happy I shall not talk about it. Three—a charming number; one that satisfies the mind. There are the three points of analysis; it is the best of three in championships; there are the three Graces. You see how my hidden love of order and method (coming from my Teutonic origins, no doubt) gives itself away in the smallest details.

So there were three. The second was spoilt by a self-confrontation, however imperfect it may have been, and a want of naturalness. The natural way would have been to leave one another without any kind of fuss, body and heart quite satisfied and ready for other adventures. There was nothing between us other than that short, sticky, spring-time affection, the bursting of buds, the delight of the suddenly clean-swept purified air. We were young and free

75

for the first time. It was a one-season's love. Faced with the equinox it is no use looking sour; nor must one stop the flowers from opening.

But as I have said, we were no longer natural. We wanted to be *in love*. What we meant by that I no more know now than I did then : I suppose that we just wanted it 'to last a little longer'. We were upsetting the order of nature and we were putting no other order in its place. The result was a harvest lost. It might have been foreseen.

But I wanted to talk about my first love. That one was perfectly natural and savage. I loved, and I gave myself right away; and I would easily have killed to have been with the man I loved—I mean that literally. As I have said, the man himself was by no means natural. Yet in his own way he loved me—a rather fatherly way, rather perverse, rather schoolmasterly (he took endless pains to teach me quantities of things which were very useful to me, and he sent me off, at the age of twenty and provided with a baby, to improve myself a little more at the Sorbonne). Furthermore, I was a good subject for a schoolmaster.

I have never known any man who has not taught me something. From the first I learnt about Paris, the things one has to know not to be absurd, how to talk, how to write, and how to look natural when one is natural, which is twice as hard. And that there are clothes one must not buy, even though one may long for them very much. The only thing he was never able to teach me was not to grow sleepy early on in the evening. I dozed at first nights, dozed at the Elysée-Club when the stars were going by, dozed at night-clubs . . . He had to give up making me lead a truly Parisian life.

There was a man who taught me to eat really good food and not to blush under the stern and splendid gaze of head waiters. There was a man who taught me to eat chips on greasy paper tablecloths and to answer the cracks of dangerously cheerful working-men. There was a man who taught me how to look at paintings, and a woman too who taught me how to talk about them (a little).

The world was full of delightful objects. I learnt about cars and also about scooters behind absurd and charming young men from Saint-Germain-des-Prés. I learnt to smoke, and to drink a little. But as I never felt the need for it, I never drank to a really romantic extent. In hotel bedrooms I learnt to call people *toi*, and I learnt a vast, all-embracing kindness for men—men sweating or coughing, handsome or ugly, sunburnt or pale, who all smoked after they had made love. The time of shady hotels with their creaking lifts and dangling wallpaper is past, but I have never forgotten that kindness.

Men: the things they talked about, politics or football, occasionally writing: their liking for café pavements, their pride in their car or their silk or nylon shirt, and yet holes in their socks nevertheless and sometimes dirty nails . . . I learnt all that, and I loved it. I was Valéry Larbaud's Mousarion (not knowing Lucien, I left it to Larbaud to point it out to me), 'gentle and kind to men'. Now that I am one man's woman and nothing else, I still do not forget those men with their armour off, not one of whom was quite unworthy of being loved.

I learnt all that, as I say. Afterwards I met my third love, who taught me to use all that I had learnt. But I am not going to talk about that. All the time that I was learning these things, my first love was dying, slowly stifling. That went on for several years, for it was hard to kill. Sometimes I would cry as I felt something that could not be grasped dwindling and vanishing between my hands, though I did not know whether I really wanted to hold it back. His brief affairs and mine, which at first I accepted without thinking about them, moved us away from one another in time. I would not have liked talking about it; so we kept quiet. This silence was a tear that slowly parted the stuff of our life into two pieces. I admired him, I loved him still, although he was already another person, just as the traveller to whom you write is a person

77

other than the one you said good-bye to at the station barely an hour ago.

I could still make attempts at coming closer; he could accept them, in his own manner: they were bricks piling up on an abandoned building-site, building material from which nothing would ever be made. Each time I did so I was looking unknowingly for the pleasure, the relief that I felt in collecting the words that would make a poem, the impressions that would be useful in a novel. No doubt it was because the first enthusiasm had passed that this love gave me a feeling of purposelessness. But the day was to come when all these repeatedly piled-up outbursts of feeling were also to be discarded material, vacant lots, saddening rough sketches and graceful scaffolding. I felt vaguely that I wanted to think of something else and of someone else. When I went off on my journey I left that love behind me. I had a vague hope that I should not find it when I came back, that someone would have got rid of it for me, that the house would be empty. It was.

And yet I had loved that man. He was a real man, brave and intelligent. I had admired him and feared him. I had been proud of his strength and his intelligence, and I had wanted to see him triumph over other men. I had hated those he hated and loved those he loved. I had repeated his words without understanding them, and I had worn clothes chosen by him although I did not like them. I had followed his advice and I had adopted his principles. What more could I have done, being the kind of person I was? And how had it happened that a love like this had trickled away between my fingers? Was it these principles, that I had taken over out of a desire to please, out of confidence and love, which were separating us now?

And where did it come from, this need for purpose, for lastingness, for building, in a person like myself, so little aware and so little given to reflexion? Was it not from this work, which I had carried out conscientiously every morning since my adolescence and which, by its imperatives and its joys, had taught me other

78

imperatives and had given me the need for other joys? My friend of those days liked to see me work. He liked orderliness and application, and the best side of his love for me was in that desire that he had for my 'success'. But the best of his love struggled against the worst, and at last destroyed it. Friend of those days, who might have been the only one, you should never have taught me to build, to arrange, to create. You should not have praised patience, steadiness and discipline. Friend, whose name hurts and will always hurt a little, you should never have taught me to write if you did not also teach me to love. Orderliness is catching.

PART TWO

THE BOSS is rock-like, a washed-out-blue stone mass with edges made of hard fat—the folds of his chin, for example, are squared off, rigid, without the slightest concession to softness : rather well done. His arms are thick with hard fat, yellow fat, tight, fine-grained; his belly under its apron is overbearing, with no hint of that notion of ludicrous and somewhat touching weakness (gluttony, sloth) that a belly can bring to mind; no, a stone belly, and the stoniness extends even to the apron, fixed in unchanging folds by filth that reeks of disinfectant : the boss is monolithic, set there like a stone by a decree of nature, with his over-sized Easter Island head, its simplified features black and huge in the half-darkness of the big room, the vast mouth making a right-angle, and above all that sightless eye, a round, a simple round.

Uncouth divinity of the absurd : that at least is what he would like to be, and in his great moments of rage, with his thundering voice belching out its oracles, oracles launched from an impassive mask, he succeeds; he wipes out the tell-tale lines in his face, the human quivering, even the gestures that he thinks would make him approachable : with his fists closed but not tightened, hanging on either side of his pointed belly, his empty statue's eyes, and with his mouth open, a speaking-trumpet above the folds of his chin, he turns the whole of himself into an imprecatory stone.

You should see the working of this machine as it gets under way. First thing in the morning, ritual gestures—the bar wiped

with a greasy cloth, the sawdust spread upon the floor, which will
be swept by the whining Perséphone, his spouse, who is still in bed
and who will appear yawning, a bleary-eyed Breton lobster; first
cups of coffee, first words. The Boss asserts himself as Boss, describes himself before he sets about existing, as for a moment he
gazes upon the new neon installation before lighting it with the
gesture of a creator.

the boss's monologue

As for me, I take care of myself. Bar-keepers don't live long.
They don't take care of themselves. I do take care of myself. First,
a rare steak in the morning. [He moves his huge head defiantly,
but no one takes up the challenge.] In the morning. And some
milk. MILK! That gets me going. In here, from seven in the
morning on, I see them coming in—little squirts, types with their
liver all anyhow, shot to pieces. You want a glass of white? There
you are. A Pernod? I pour it out. A red, full right up? All right,
ruin your liver. I don't give a ——— : it's you who pay. I drink
MILK! Understand?

At mid-day, spuds and something properly cooked, yes : but no
wine. That stuns you. The bar-keeper, he lets them buy him
drinks, he's hail fellow and so on. Not me! If you want a drink
you pay for it and I'll pay for my own, see? Leave me alone : I
do my job, and all the rest is no concern of mine. If everybody
was like me, there would be less bleeding trouble in the world.
Everyone in his own place and that's an end of it. You don't like
it? A bomb in the middle of the lot of you. No one any the wiser.
These bastards are up to anything.

When his rhetorical exercises are over, he allows us the neon
lights. A furtive shadow, a middle-aged woman with a shopping-
basket, comes into the café, hesitates, takes advantage of the complicated working of the coffee-machines to glide in the direction
of the lavatory, that temptation. But slowly the omnipresent boss

turns, and in a skilful crescendo his fine bass rises little by little. "What will you bet she doesn't have a drink? I know the type: there's no shortage of them round here. Wears gloves, gives herself airs, and doesn't have a drink, not even a God-forsaken coffee. Just you wait and see."

The woman with the basket reappears amidst total silence: all this notice startles her. She slips between two tables, passes in front of the bar with her shoulders hunched (she is a woman of about fifty, decently clothed, decently equipped with spectacles, gloves and a hint of a moustache), knocks into a customer, takes on an offended air, and under the cover of this attitude carries out her retreat in a masterly fashion.

Slowly the boss runs his satisfied gaze over his audience. (A mechanic at the bar, two men with brief-cases and a pair of lovers in the body of the café. And me, in a corner, with my papers.)

"Bleeding swindler! What did I tell you? Not even a coffee. Not even a glass of wine! It's enough to disgust you with life. Even so, a glass of wine would never cover my overheads. What about the water? What about the paper? The lavatories are looked after properly in my place! What about the servant? And the nuisance? Every time anyone goes through there [there are two doors] it sends a draught right over my feet. And for all I know she may look up something in the directory. There it is: I can't lock it up: but it is there *for the customers*! A slight difference, I believe. And [*the crowning horror*] suppose she uses the soap? Yes, sir, it can reach that pitch. There are some of these women—it's nearly always women: a man would never have the nerve—there are some who do actually wash their hands! Why not get into my bath, while they are about it? Oh, so long as there are still Jews in France [*or* Arabs, *according to what day it is*]!

There he is, geared into his day and running. So am I. For I patiently wait for these first (inevitable) shouts to gear myself into my own personal day. First coffee (or tea, *according to what day it is*), first cigarette; I take my papers out of my brief-case; the juke-box does not worry me too much—you get used to it; and I drift far from the boss. Now and then a cry louder than the rest makes me raise my head : distraction; a moment's pause. The boss always delights me, like those natural phenomena (rainbows, storms, tides) whose real, visible existence one never tires of verifying over and over again.

A customer complains that the coffee is bad : "Why don't you have it at home, then?" A passer-by says that the direction that the boss gave him yesterday was wrong: "If that street existed at all, it would be where I said. If it is not there, that is because it doesn't exist." The question is dealt with, like all questions that he deigns to consider.

He is passionately attached to the determinate, the absurd, the ultimate. This passion leads him on to bold sophistries, to reasonings that make one stretch one's eyes. If a customer disagrees with one of his favourite maxims, "Bastard, Bastard and Co., that's what the police are," he replies without any hesitation, "The proof is that one of my friends is a cop. He's a friend; but he's a bastard." Who can answer an argument like that? No one.

Calm reigns in Absurdia; the boss presides at his counter, and as he dispenses coffee, as he produces the bills to the pleasant sound of the cash-register, so he also pours forth definition, solution, nomenclature, all of it set down once and for all in who knows what mysterious statutes, what Book of Wisdom, as unchanging as his features, his life. Beyond the Law, personal peculiarities do not exist. "You are in the artistic line; you don't have to worry with all this."

I agree, not choosing to argue. Besides, for me the formidable divinity is protective, sometimes even lyrical. "Ah, you're very lucky, buried in your papers; you're above all this, floating in the air . . ." *This* is the price of coffee, the war in Indo-China (in those days it was not yet the war in Algeria), the taxes and his daughter who-has-got-herself-put-in-the-family-way, and the girls who will no longer go into service because they are looked after—and you should see how they are looked after—in the factories, and they are all communists . . .

I was lucky; I was outside all this, all this which was 'life, don't you see?' and I let him alone while he busies himself with it, slapping on his labels, slapping them on as hard as ever he can: "Jews, niggers, cops, artists, politicians, Judases, bastards," and many more, all subject to unchanging laws and a thoroughly satisfying determinism. Special peculiarities, nil. Why not?

For my part, I too had a law; very elementary, no doubt, over-simple, reduced almost to nothing by the banishment of everything that I had been able to learn and unlearn here and there. Still, it was a law, and it had some relationship to the terms that I had been taught. Right and wrong; work; good and bad behaviour . . .

As far as I was concerned, good behaviour meant work, getting up at half past six, pencil on paper: evil was the newspaper that one dawdles over before having worked, the morning lost in gossip and the whole day after it—for in fact my discipline arose from the paucity of my virtue, and my hurry to get up, to throw myself upon the blank page, from my extreme frailty: the slightest temptation, such as a detective story lying about, too long a walk in the streets or the beginning of a game with my son, would instantly turn into a sofa for my idleness to loll upon. So, with my virtue arising from my lack of virtue, I worked harder than many people do, and that is a fact.

Work done, I floated in the air, became rarified; I no longer existed, and between me and myself there was no longer any link, none between the long and painstaking morning and the end of the afternoon lounged away in a cinema, wasted in stupid talk, and sometimes carried on (sometimes, not always, not often, neither too much nor too little—neither *dolce vita* nor juvenile delinquent, nor virtuous struggle, but just as it happened) in a five-hundred-francs-an-hour hotel (financial difficulties: so, friends in poverty, we turned our purses upside down—and there still had to be enough to buy cigarettes): an hotel left in haste, I might add. For suddenly catching up with me, the dread of not sleeping enough, of losing a morning's work, would throw a bridge between the evening and the morning, stick the two halves of myself together again and hurry me to the nearest underground—the end of that 'freedom' or rather of that vacillation. In the end it was tiring to be

cut in two

Yes, because as I was sitting in the Café Longchamp in the avenue de Neuilly at a quarter past seven—I was writing my first book amidst the jangling of the pin-table, the whistling of the coffee-machine, the smell of sawdust and the white wine they drink at dawn (one after another the customers were swallowed up in the cold morning air—goodbye in the door-way, and once more I see their heads surrounded by their steaming breath like a saint with his halo)—patiently trying, without being too sure why, to make words catch up with their meaning, as I was writing one letter after another, and as I was making up my mind that this was to be re-done and that to be tossed out, according to a certain scale of values accepted once and for all, nevertheless, was I not after all implicitly admitting the need to catch up with myself one day?

At least I know that there was nowhere where I felt more *me* than in these little cafés, noisy or deserted, cheerful or dreary, where I was just one more customer, sitting at the table at the far end, a figure in this picture, a cog in this machine, anxiously, safely fulfilling my function, which was to write. Safety: it was not right, nor would it ever be; it had to be started over again; it was bad; but *that was what one was there for*. To start over again, to say that it was not right and to start over again once more. The anxiety did not come from that. In any case it was vague, so vague, arising from the contrast between that patient, steady, almost rhythmic effort and the ridiculous vacillation that directly followed it, a liberating feeling, really pleasant, the balloon gently rising in the air, without strain, without a rope to hold it: was it an anxiety at all?

No; I did not think about it: I was devoid of thought, sitting in a cinema with another woman, sucked up by the screen, wholly preoccupied by the satisfaction of chewing a caramel; or sitting in the library of the Sorbonne, taken up with the gymnastics of dates (I loved that); or walking in the Bois, by Bagatelle, looking at the flowers, nothing but the flowers, the flowers without aesthetic thought, without thought, the colour, the shape of the flowers; a yellow tulip, that firmness, that transparency, that stiff fragility, that strength, the sap, the fat stem, the greedy root in the moist earth, that stout foster-mother. I was a tulip and I imagined, no, I felt, a mimetic longing for damp earth into which to thrust my feet, a longing for sun, not for immaterial sun, the thought of sun, but for dripping, sugary sun, a honey of sun, stupefying, ripening, rotting. I was there living, dead, vegetable, and that ghost of uneasiness, that shadow of uneasiness very high over my head, like a cloud in the sky.

Not very worrying, after all; and what connexion could it have with thought? None. None at all. Everything was indeed cut in two, as you might put it; did that very cloud exist (it might be a pain inside, a trifling headache), was it something that belonged to me rather than a sunny exhalation of the sky or the after-effects of flu? When I was working there was no cloud. When I was not working there was one: there you are. Another me floating like an ectoplasm, perhaps. (I wonder whether there is a cloud over the boss. Maybe that is the cause of his perpetual anger. And I know what this cloud might appear to signify: 'The eye was in the grave and it looked at Cain.' The whole difference lies in the intent: the eye looks, whereas the cloud is satisfied with merely floating).

Nothing more innocent than a cloud, so long as you pay no

attention to it. It floats, it makes no noise, scarcely even any shade. You may quite well never notice that you are being followed by a cloud. It is not at all like the ubiquitous eye. All you have to do is not look up: there are people who are very good at that. Once you have seen it, however, whether on purpose or by accident— why then clearly it is more of a nuisance. It will not be driven away: it is there, stupid, self-satisfied, fat with rain and foul vexations. This cloud is not a symbol: you can see it perfectly well: it is . . . it is a *contraption,* as Jacques Perret would put it. Now the voice is no longer mine, but the boss's. "As for me," he says heavily, "you must not muck me about. I am a decent sort, but I must not be mucked about. All these contraptions . . ."

For him these contraptions, these thingummybobs, are not the international organizations, as they are for some, but rather distinctions, 'hanky-panky', relationships . . . "You aren't from round here, so you don't know a bleeding thing." (The final reply, the bludgeon-like argument administered to someone who voices a different political opinion.) But the sharp and scornful customer is not put down. "So I'm not from round here, and what the hell does that amount to? My money isn't from round here either, but you lap it up."

The boss is struck dumb, filled with an uneasiness that is not unrelated to mine when he is faced with an apparently insoluble question. His heavy wits revolve the seemingly harmless crack, beneath which he senses a subtle poison. Distrust, then impotent rage, then rejection. According to the time of day and the boss's temper, the awkward customer will be called cop, bleeder, Jew or bastard. The main thing is to insulate the radioactive *contraption,* the phrase that makes you think, in the radiation-proof envelope of a thoroughly enclosing definition.

Why always talk about the boss? Because every day he is there again in front of me, sitting behind his till, behind his blue-canvas-covered belly, asserting with all his fat, all hard, set, parcelled out into pounds and distributed in an orderly manner over his vast frame, asserting with his pillar-like legs, asserting with his aggressive belly, asserting with his square torso, asserting with his big yellow head, asserting with his slow, solemn arms, whose culminating point is the fist (often brought down, without feverish haste, upon the counter; or unfolding into an open palm, the spread fingers standing out), asserting not stupidity, but the desire, the determination, to be stupid. I admit it : the boss fascinates me.

If it were no more than his way of saying "go to the sausage-factory", as one says "go to the john".

It is the only moment in the day (it happens around a quarter past ten in the morning, between the late coffees and the early apéritifs) at which his voice takes on a shade of poetic feeling. And his wife, complaining, drabble-tailed, dawdling for two hours behind the curtain (crocheted unbleached thread—one of the last in Paris), in her slow Breton voice, "Look, there's a Negro . . . Isn't he black . . ." Then, gazing at the floor and at the ooze The floorcloth sends in runnels at her feet (forgive me : this woman does inspire blank verse) : "I'd rather be as old as I am," she murmurs, another Ophelia, "than have to live . . ."

Unwell, voluntarily unwell, continually afflicted with colds and pains, her sufferings, like the boss's stupidity, answer as an alibi for her, a boudoir. She withdraws into it, surrounded by a little court of rheumatisms, neuralgias and insomnias, and against these, with a beauty-queen's listlessness, she faintly encourages a troop of rivals—Belladonna, Pyramidon, and others of the Aspirin tribe, who provide her with imaginary company far more agreeable than the wanton creature from the milk-shop or the humble news-paper woman with her chapped fingers.

She hardly sees them as they sit there, the one crossing her fat white legs high and the other blowing on her red fingers to warm them. But she condescends to give them the latest account, after the style of Saint-Simon, rather for her own sake than for her listeners, who are incapable of understanding her : "I had such insomnia last night ! First I took Belladenal—usually that works for me. Not a bit of it! So I said to myself, it's the Pyramidon that's keeping me awake, I said; I took it too late, I said; and then I'd already had the Sulfarem at two o'clock, because of the sweetbreads I couldn't digest yesterday . . ."

The red-haired milk-woman pretends to listen and furtively watches the absent-minded customer who does not see her leg—more and more of it is exhibited, until it can be seen as far as the place where the shining stocking squeezes the soft flesh too tightly. But the newspaper-seller misses not a word of the fascinating chronicle, and overcome by this dream for ever beyond her reach, she murmurs, "Ah, when you are ill, you are never bored . . ."

Every day, or almost every day, I am there, patiently trying to match words and their meaning, trying to find—to rediscover—balance, proportion, a truth : I don't know . . . Every day. This was the time when I could reply to the question, "And when you stop working, every day at the same time, do you not think about it any more?", and quite sincerely say, "No." Sincerely and even rather proudly.

For although it is true that once it is past noon I no longer think about this work whose meaning I do not know, and whose aim I have not defined, it is also true that I do not choose to think about it. Barrier: door of this café or another closed, and on the other side of it Prudence, Patience and Perseverance, lovely characters from the *Roman de la Rose*, wait with their friend Attentiveness, for the disinfectant-smelling mornings of tomorrow. Perhaps they wait with an allegorical Me, a me-of-between-seven and-eleven-a.m. while an afternoon-me, free from all anxiety, all preoccupation, drifts along the hours, drifts as one sleeps . . .

The boss and his wife walk about like this the whole day long, dangerous sleep-walkers, apt to bite if you wake them up. I watch them without waking them. I watch myself (from noon on) without waking myself, either. It is perfectly easy at first, then not so easy, then impossible. You need an iron will to shut yourself into sleep: above all when you have the ingrained habit of waking up for a moment every morning. Always this comic double game. I used to watch the boss playing it; I played it myself, and I still hoped to get away with it. And I presumed to talk about falsehood! Presumed to describe the liar! I presumed to imagine him, shut up in his inner room, spinning his cocoon, completely sheltered, a rat inside his soundproof, smellproof cheese, letting in nothing but objects and thoughts divorced from all connexion with life, concocted by himself alone from ingredients supplied only by himself . . .

He writes a book, experiences a love-affair, joins a party or a religion : if he is less concerned with accepted form, he romances, adopts irrelevance as his rule of life. But whatever the surroundings, he is always quite shut away, thoroughly protected by his carapace, whatever its shape or colour may be. Every knob hides a secret, no doubt (sometimes a wretched, childish little secret), and every different shade another : but how varied is not the outcome!

With what zoological curiosity do we not gaze upon these outward armours in the form of lizards, armadillos, unicorns; sometimes almost with admiration! For falsehood has its own graces, its own system of aesthetics. Sometimes it is almost inspired, with only a slight obliquity to deprive it of the beauty of truth : sometimes it is grotesque, proliferating, with the overflowing richness of gargoyles. It imitates the forms of nature with extraordinary skill, and it turns determinist the better to remain impregnable.

But its essential characteristic is that it is shut up. *It is shut up,* I wrote, as, writing of an animal I should have put, *It is brown,* or of an object, *It is tall.* And I also wrote this : Falsehood is on a single plane: yes, it literally flattens out, levels, simplifies; yes, even when it proliferates, overflows, takes every form; it simplifies because it is *related to nothing.*

I wrote that, and I wrote it in the café, and I wrote a book called *House of Lies,* and I planned a book that was to be called *Café Céleste* (because of that scrap of truth that each person seems to me to bear within himself : but not many people understood this title), and I worked in this café and people said to me, "Still escaping then?" And at home the maid, speaking of my husband, "He forgets everything : yes, he's a real artist . . ."

And I did not ask myself, "Is an artist not related to anything?" Furthermore, I did not ask myself, "What is an artist?"either; nor even, "What is art?" in spite of the questions put to me on the subject. Why should I have an opinion on art?

Because it was my calling? But (I said to myself at that time) it is also my calling to have a husband and some children and to read manuscripts and to decide what the household shall eat; and do people expect me to have theories on those subjects? They don't, do they? Well, then.

Still, it is to be hoped that I am more of a writer than a housewife. "I am a writer, as I might be a shoemaker," I said. There was a great deal of pride in that. I still think, "I chose doing this, as I might have chosen to be a shoemaker if I had thought that I was only good enough to make shoes." I also think, "If I were only good enough to be a shoemaker, and if I had chosen to be one, I should still be myself, and I should have just the same value that I have now." I have chosen to write novels. I have chosen to write *my* novels. We shall see. Still I must not be expected to have views on art.

At the most I might have some uneasiness upon the subject to clear up, as usual. For example, when I read a piece 'on art', it often happens that I feel the same very slight uneasiness that tells me that I do not like a face that I have glimpsed or a phrase that I have heard. I have the habit of thinking about these little discords; and thinking, whatever the subject may be, carries one further than one supposes. I cannot disguise the fact that this habit of thinking is getting worse. Now all the many little uneasinesses one stumbles upon in the course of the day—an oddment in the paper, a tone you suddenly notice in a friend's voice, something you do without thinking about it, a colour, a sound, a phrase in a book—insist upon being examined, looked at, understood and perhaps classified. Otherwise when some little fact, set aside and buried since childhood and patiently taken up again the next day or in twenty years time, at last comes to the surface it will finally take its place in an organized paradise.

I like precision, and I always have liked it. I remember as a child my laborious delight with sums that 'came out', that always, whatever happened, 'came out'. Always! So an addition was done for ever and ever! The idea entranced me. And when I first began to *see* painting I rediscovered that same delight when I was in the Louvre, standing in front of a tall Byzantine Virgin, as distinct as a number, about whom, in an intangible order, were ranged great mathematical angels. That was the word that came to me; and for me it was a word of adoration. I had discovered another proof, as well as that of my sums. And I at once conceived the truth as a kind of sum, but one in which the numbers had colour. An obvious fact, quite simple, but matchless and inexplicable, for it could only be stated, no more.

An obvious fact . . . And earlier I had supposed that truth was not the same for everybody; that sin and virtue (if these good old words, fallen out of currency since the *Roman de la Rose* can still be used) were not alike for all. Is that a mathematical certainty? Here was an inconsistency in which I could not readily see which side I was on. Was my logic, my precious logic, deserting me?

But let us carry on according to my usual method, which consists of having none. Let us leave the acrobat hanging high over the net between two trapezes and let us stay in the Louvre talking about art. Who knows but what our conversation may provide us with the impetus needed to start the interrupted leap once more? Let us walk on, amidst the cries of the attendants exchanging confidential shouts about food from one room to an-

other, amidst the guffaws of the little girls before the anatomical
revelations, amidst the rather plump women in spectacles and
worn, too-tight skirts who explain in German, English and Nor-
wegian that no one knows why the glaucous Gioconda is smiling.
(But unlikely though it seems these good ladies, thumping out in
their strange tongues the one syllable understood by all : *Sex*, have
taught me that the background of green water and rocks has a
Freudian meaning.) There is always less noise round the Primitives. Why? Perhaps because of good taste. Yet I hear a young
American murmur, as he leads his wife away, "Oh, these are all
alike. They're all saints . . ."

I love this little Calvary of the Siennese school and its deliberate
immobility. It is not a representation of the Crucifixion; it is an
explanation of it. And a phrase comes into my mind, one of those
uneasiness-phrases that wait in my memory, smiling like the
Cheshire Cat, to be worked out one day by me. "Great art is that
which makes us say, *That's just it*, when the whole point is that
it is not *it* at all, but art." It was Claude Roy, so often admirably
and poetically exact, who wrote that phrase which leaves me
wondering. This holy woman who turns away her head, not with
horror, but with a movement that *means* horror, seems to bear
him out. So does this soldier who is pointing at the scene, like an
actor who ends the piece and draws its moral. And that Virgin
in her traditional prostration, who is not suffering (as a Renaissance Virgin might suffer, in her own flesh and in ours), but who
represents (but perhaps also embodies?) a universal anguish.

She certainly appears to bear him out, and yet . . . These little
figures are certainly not human beings : yet they stand for human
beings and human feelings, as the letter A stands for a sound but
is not one. Is that where art lies? Would the letter A be art, and
the sound A, the cry A, life? The word or the colour art, and the
unnamed thing, the raw thing itself, life? But why not the other
way about? Or both ways at once? Or the relationship of the one
to the other? Yes, sooner that. Sooner that.

Forgive me these slow approaches. In all sincerity I am looking for the object of my inquiry. And this inquiry does not prevent me from taking the most spontaneous pleasure in looking at this Herod's Banquet, a minute fifteenth-century picture in which the entirety of the vivid old tale does not unfold but rather exists all in the same moment, doing away with time. For while Salome dressed in a grievous pink is still dancing under an absinthe-green canopy (dancing, motionless, held by an invisible lens, dances and *is* the word dance, both at once—a smooth, free-flowing down-stroke), the grey headsman on the left already has his sword raised to take off the head, the already bleeding head that a pleasant-looking red-legged blue soldier is bringing in the middle of the picture.

"The whole point is that it is not *it* at all, but art . . ." As you see, Claude, I put the ball at your feet. Still, that phrase always pulls me up, leaves me wondering. It shuts art away, makes it a thing apart, isolates it, confines it within its 'speciality', like Guy shutting off poetry, never allowing it to settle; like the coarse feeders of politics putting the 'intellectuals' to silence with their gross laughter; like those whom you do not like, Claude, and whom I do not like, and who entrench themselves behind such sayings as 'Politics and morals are two different things' and 'Art is not the same as good feelings'. The eternal alibi of specialization. And the *it* which is not art, what is it? Life, reality. Something else. No; I do not like that phrase. "That's all right in books; but it's not real life," say prudent parents to their daughters.

Let us go back to the polished floors of the Louvre. Long before us a philosopher observed how few people come to museums to look at the pictures. They come, and they come in numerous herds, many-tongued and strangely dressed, to make sure that the Gioconda is really there, there where they had been told, in the Louvre; to make sure that it is in fact the Uffizi that shelters Botticelli's Primavera and the Vatican the Laocoon. A glance at the guide, a glance at the bottom of the picture (number 36,633,

96

the Gioconda; that's right), and perhaps, if they are really conscientious, an enveloping glance to make sure that it is really the
same Gioconda as the one on the kitchen calendar or the repro-
duction in the 'lounge'.

It would be quite safe to bet that these painstaking little guide-
book tickers are no more sharp-sighted in life : all the time they
must certainly be saying to themselves, "Ah, that over there must
be love . . . this, old age . . ." It is a good thing they have reference
numbers. Undoubtedly for them art is one thing and life another.
Art is number 36,633, the framed picture hung in the long gallery
that smells of floor-polish; and life is their neighbour in the next
flat, a lady who might perfectly well be called La Gioconda and
who might have a sideways smile. Yet of course, the picture and
the lady have nothing to do with one another.

Still, this is rather obvious. For the woman seen by Leonardo
(before he took up his brush) and the woman seen by her neighbour would indeed be two quite distinct things; and with the
picture finished, varnished, delivered, that would make three.
And with the little private picture mirrored every day in the pupil
of her husband's or her lover's eye, if she has one, that would make
four or five. But which is the real Gioconda among them all? The
everyday-life-Gioconda? (As they say about so many actresses,
'Oh, in everyday life, you know, she is not at all like that!') The
Gioconda-Leonardo's-model? The Gioconda in the next-door
flat; the Gioconda hostess at a business dinner opposite her husband; the Gioconda lying back one day upon an illicit pillow.
One is tempted to reply *all of them*, or *none*. And that too would
be too simple. What makes everything complicated for me is that
I cannot believe that truth is the reverse of falsehood, its contrary,
its shadow or its sun. Is there in fact an everyday-life-Gioconda
at all?

Still, it is an idea that makes me think. Because after all if there
is no Gioconda (or if she is multiplied to infinity by the countless
viewpoints), why paint her? How can she be painted? Why write,

if the object of one's writing slips away and if it has no essential being of its own? If it has no essential being, at least the painter or the writer can give it a form, define it? But in that case one would have to suppose that they themselves exist, or at least believe that they do so. And that the object painted or described, if it has no truth of its own, contains their truth. Surely one of the two, the painter or the model, must exist, for the brush's work to have any meaning?

I find it all very difficult. I am sure that it has all been settled long ago by some philosopher. But what interests me is finding out what I think about it, without the help of any philosophy. Not that I scorn this help, but with neither pride nor humility I admit that I am unable to make use of it. I never did philosophy at school, and I have not been able to bring myself to it since. To begin with in the days of my innocence I said "Why should I?" And once that time was over, it was too late to start learning a new stock of words; and besides I want to live according to my own lights and see where I shall finish up.

And let us go back to that moment at which the Gioconda-wife and the Gioconda-picture are face to face, the moment when the husband has been brought it, when he does indeed come in, shake the painter by the hand, gaze, exclaim, enchanted (always supposing that he was enchanted), "It is exactly like her!" There we have art thoroughly cut off from life by a single word (but a banker's word). For of course the man knows perfectly well that it is not 'exactly like', that his wife is not that ambiguous inhabitant of a lake-settlement; he knows it just as well as those caretakers who swoon over a crewel-work sunset, with the obligatory stuffed stag belling—"How well imitated!" or "How like it is!"

Imitation implies artifice; likeness unlikeness. The delight arises as much from the one as from the other—whether it is like or whether it is not. Transposition, contrivance, organization. In any case separation. Everything seems to prove it. This does not satisfy me. Like all kinds of partitioning, it makes me feel that there is something wrong.

And this same uneasiness suddenly brings me back to a restaurant (Le Vefour, to be exact), at the moment when a perfectly anonymous head-waiter pours fruity wine into my glass.

I was lunching with a wealthy man who was very fond of talking. As I am very fond of listening, it seems to me an excellent combination. And yet I never leave him without an uneasiness, one that I associate with the word 'art', because every time I say to myself (with that sadness that an indifferent digestion easily brings into being), "There is no doubt about it; I do not like art." What a feeling of guilt! And I feel it again now that I have begun to talk about art: I am afraid of boring my neighbour, because I find it boring myself. I have never been much interested in art as a 'subject', and the people who talk about it often bore me. So it would be much better for me to talk about a

luncheon with M.B.

since it will come to the same thing after all. Everything comes together and meets in me today. It is the joy and the despair of my life. It is also the reason for my discouragement in writing this book: shall I ever be done with it? Never mind: let us have lunch. I always lunch too well with Marcel B. (yes indeed, it is the same Marcel). It is not that I particularly want to lunch well. In fact I do not really want to lunch at all, being on a diet. But I am so sure that he looks forward to entertaining the poor starving writer splendidly (he says "standing treat," by the way: "On Saturday I stood So-and-So treat,") that I am compelled to swallow the *oeufs bénédictine* that I loathe and that will go straight to my liver.

He at least is in full bloom from the very beginning of the meal. He is carrying out some business deal that has brought him to Paris; he is relaxing in the company of a writer whom he alone appreciates (for he takes particular care to assure me that my books are not in the least successful and that he alone understands them; he quotes me X's adverse criticism, has not read Y's kind words—but Y is a fool, and besides his conduct in 1940 . . .); and lastly he talks about art.

He talks about art because of his delight in it. Perhaps I might say that he talks about art by divine vocation. He has a vocation to be an amateur, a lover of art. He paints a little, sometimes writes, but without ambition; for him it is just in order to "break down the technique". But he is unbeatable as an amateur. He makes the journey to Leningrad just to see the Hermitage. He remembers (I don't) that little Turner on the right at the far end of the little room in the Uffizi; yesterday he saw Audiberti's latest play and found time to spend half an hour in the storage galleries of the Louvre (he can get in, having contacts), or in front of the Rubens that you just have to see because otherwise you know nothing at all about Rubens; and then, at the Galerie de France —he only darted in for a moment—he saw a Manessier which . . .

All this culture, all this eagerness to see, read, admire, is worthy of respect. I have to repeat that to myself ten times over so as to be able to bear it. Yet after all if there were no people like that, who would buy books? I cannot tell why, but still the idea does not please me. My liver is already feeling the *oeufs bénédictine* and I am going to have to tackle the *canard au sang* which I do not want in the very least; but it was Marcel who ordered, for in this too he likes showing his capabilities.

It is not only museums that he goes to see; he visits famous cellars too, and compares one wine with another, recognizes the year, or seems to recognize it, for no one ever contradicts him when, having sniffed a Bordeaux, he tells the head-waiter that of course he spots the 1937 Montrachet. He talks a great deal about *the art of living*. He says, "Oh the blue of that . . . This wine has a bouquet . . . The wonderful passage in which . . ."

He does not say it to show off; he really does like this wine, this

book, this picture; and he knows why and explains the reason
quite well. He is a man perfectly capable of going fifty miles out
of his way to see a single painting or to try a little inn that he has
heard praised. It is touching. I am his little inn : he discovered
me and he is very fond of me. I am sure that he says to his friends
in Bordeaux, "There is only one thing that can be read this month,
and that is Mallet-Joris. The passage in which . . ." And no doubt
his friends listen to him just as I do when he tells me, so con-
fidently and with so much pleasure, "There is only one thing that
can be drunk with this duck, and that is . . ."

I drink. I shall be very unwell. And I shall be unhappy because
I have not seen the Manessier show—I who live in Paris, have
not read the latest Faulkner (but Marcel will certainly give me
such a complete and massive summary of it in the course of the
meal that I never shall read it), because I do not often go to the
Louvre (though I do go sometimes, as I have proved earlier on),
and because I will not have enjoyed this conversation about art.
I really do not know why I go on lunching with Marcel B. every
time he comes to Paris. I think it is in fact because of the uneasiness that I derive from him, and which I cannot manage to define.
I have a certain persistance in trying to understand that serves me
instead of intelligence.

Marcel comes in, busy, well-dressed : he likes being recognized
by the attendants and the head-waiters; it is a not uncommon
characteristic and there is nothing blameworthy about it. Men of
over fifty really must be allowed to have some pleasures left. He
is delighted to see me. He gives me his hand, casts a piercing
glance at my dress and in an amused tone points out that it is no
longer fashionable. It does not put him out. Indeed I might say
that it gives him a certain kind of pleasure. He would not even
dislike displaying me in rags in one of the most luxurious places
in Paris. It would be a way of showing that he is above these
things, above the trifling pleasure of being seen with a pretty,
well-dressed woman.

I must be fair : these hypothetical rags would also be for him a means of asserting the pre-eminent rank of the things of the spirit. M.B. is quite rich, I believe, without being fabulously wealthy. But he does not respect the 'bourgeois values'. He says so. He proves it : he asks writers out, feeds painters, provides clothes for a sculptor who runs off with the silver from his country house. Marcel bears him no grudge. He considers this adventure picturesque, as he considers it picturesque that my dress should be out of fashion. At the drop of a hat he would blame it for not being out of date enough.

And with the same amused smile he asks after my children. If I had a litter of young cheetahs, he would inquire after them in exactly the same way. And through me he sends them an immense bag of monkey-nuts—I mean of sweets with the likeness of the Marquise de Sévigné upon them. Uneasiness. This time, I say to myself, I shall seize it; I shall grasp this uneasiness that flees like a little animal in the woods. "Now we must arrange what we are going to eat . . . Let's see : I think *oeufs bénédictine* to begin with . . . Don't you think so? With a white wine, but not one of those wines that . . ."

There is nothing for it but to let him choose. It is his calling, after all. I am not going to teach him how to arrange a meal, when it is quite clear that he understands the business better than I do. I watch him. Tall, lean and wiry; somewhat overflowing gestures; cordial way of speaking; a lively glance; easiness of manner; reaches the important subjects a little too soon, open-hearted a little too soon; a certain lack of modesty, perhaps?

But come, if a man is enthusiastic . . . Eyes lively; but they shift. No, *shift* gives a notion of craftiness, and that is not what I mean at all. Eyes lively, but . . . He looks straight at you; he even looks at you intently, because he is doing his best to convince you. "You must, you absolutely must, go first thing tomorrow . . . After all, what is there to keep you from going? Oh, if I were only as lucky as you, living in Paris, and . . ." It is so obviously pointless to explain to him that one has a headache, that one is not always in a condition to look at masterpieces, that the little boy has the measles . . . Still, let us have a go.

"You see, Marcel, it is difficult, with the things I have to do . . . manuscripts to read . . . the children . . . my little Pauline, you know . . ."

I was wrong to judge him so hastily. He displays interest at once; he even asks questions. What, I only have three rooms? And I manage to work? Oh, at the café; just so. And my children are not well—how dreadful for me! No, not really quite as bad as all that. And my flat, although it is rather small, is not altogether the slum that he imagines. And my husband is not compelled to paint in the darkness, between a cradle and the kitchen range: I try to bring things back to somewhat less harrowing proportions. But he at once seizes upon my words and repeats them, and in his mouth they take on a different flavour, a subtly grating sound . . .Uneasiness. Incomprehensible.

"So, in short, yours is a commonplace life—a life like everybody else's?" he says, looking at me attentively. His attention. At least I cannot blame him for being unconcerned. I talk to him about my life; he takes it into consideration at once, inspects it, attempts to understand it with an interest that not everyone would feel. Well then?

I agree to the ordinariness of my life. He broods on it for a moment. "That also has its beauty," he says, gravely. "The little things . . . A still life by Chardin . . . Vermeer . . . Your Dutch side . . ."

I feel that he is going to quote Verlaine, I feel it, I feel it! He quotes him. "A whisp of straw in the byre . . ." The meal comes to an end. I shall always leave Marcel feeling that there is something that will never square between me and a certain conception of 'art'.

And really, when it comes to that, what have I to reproach Marcel with, poor fellow? He makes an intelligent use of his money and his leisure. He is a cultivated man, he delights in beautiful things, he is interested in 'human beings'—I think it is 'human beings' that he says, and really there is very little showing off or pretence in his liking for the 'art of living'.

What do I want, then? Business men, scarlet in the face after eating, who go off to the Folies Bergère, horse-coping skinflint cinema producers who want to make me work at cut rates, telling me, with candid eyes, that it is a pretty good piece of business, after all, *for a writer* . . ., slim and too-well-dressed publishers who bring out first novels at the author's expense, unless he happens to be a pretty boy, cinema actors who pride themselves on not being able to spell, professionally anxious left-wing intellectuals who nevertheless have good appetites, right-wing intellectuals who destroy your desire to eat as early as the hors-d'oeuvre by uttering the words "young and healthy" with their chest pushed out and their eye automatically fixed on the bottle of pills beside their glass filled with a truly French Burgundy . . . I am talking about the kind of people one might possibly be with, at the Vefour, having luncheon. There is no sort of question but that M.B. is worth much more than those people. I tell myself this and I tell myself again; and then, this uneasiness . . .

I shall go and have lunch with Marcel when he is next in Paris. We shall see. "Yes," says he, "it will be splendid to see you again. We have talked so little today . . . I wanted to say, about your book . . ."

Obviously I do not like talking about my books. Nor much about other people's. Smell of dust. I feel myself turned into a dusty volume as M.B. speaks to me. I imagine him talking about me, about my children, about my husband, about my work . . . That whole complex which for me makes up a living web, interwoven with so many other threads, perpetually changing and replenishing itself, turns into a picture under his gaze. Like the Gioconda. Mutatis mutandis, of course. Besides, he respectfully takes my preferences into account. If I dwell upon the numbers of my books that have been sold, my house in the country and my children's health, he is ready to admire a Renoir, all overflowing with health and plenty, apple-trees in blossom and a swing (because of Normandy), the golden skin of children, a straw hat flung on to a chair, softly-lit piano in the evening, well-behaved little girls, a home as soft as a feather-bed.

If I try to rectify the image by telling him of my work in Paris, life's daily worries, the smallness of the flat, measles and domestic problems, then he obediently plunges straight into a Balzacian gloom. He sees me waiting in sooty newspaper offices, standing in a queue before the counter where they pay family allowances, and in the evening clinging to my spouse, as thin and wasted as I am myself; married distress spreads out before his eyes; he imagines our quarrels, our arguments and our straitened budget (no, he does not think of Buffet; that is another of his merits—he does *not* like Buffet).

But, since we met, he has at last discovered what was wanted for me. Thank God, he has been patient: he tried and tried again, for I was difficult, and even rebellious; he did not grow weary, but went from the one extreme to the other, from Daumier to Van Gogh, from Proust (my health!) to Hemingway (my *romantic* past, as he sees it . . .); and at last he made his discovery and he is as happy as one who has brought an important piece of work to a successful end, who has put the last touch to something he has created—Chardin.

From now onwards that is the key word. He will be able to talk about me with his mind at rest: "An entirely commonplace life; a modest competence . . ." The more these words are despised and this kind of life dis-esteemed, the more he will polish them; a hundred times he will re-touch his work, and he will end up with this delightfully balanced, restrained yet luminous Chardin, these three leeks and this jug set on a brown table (and what more modest colour is there than this brown, what richer in effulgence : brown as honey is brown, and yet golden . . .).

There I am, once and for all, in Marcel B.'s museum. He is an artist. One might say of him, as one says it of a milliner, that "he has run it up out of nothing." Yes; he is an artist. I am not sure that I like artists.

I have never really much believed in my old servant's touching myth of the "artist-who-forgets-everything", a tolerably sickening stock figure. But as I say this I find that I do not completely believe in this "good craftsman always on time", either, this creature that I seem to be (which I am too) and which has earned me the liking of my friend Luc, of the godly papers (some of them), and of all those who are in favour of partitions and specialization, including the dear basic communists (not the others, who constitute our New Aristocracy, as —— would say : a pretty hotch-potch!)

Neither a creature of inspiration nor a craftsman? What then? Both the one and the other? Responsible *and* irresponsible? Committed *and* in the clouds? Does one think about all that when one is writing? When one stops writing has one finished living? "He's a friend, but he's a swine." The Boss, always the Boss. Specialization. Luc and the bird. Poetry. I wonder whether Luc, happening to find himself with the Boss, would be aware of some touch of kin between them.

Yet things must be kept thoroughly distinct. As we have been told time and again, good writing is not made with good feelings. And it is true. Literature is made with literature. With talent, if you would prefer. But apart from talent, which is either given or not given, what is a book fed with if not with this patience, care and integrity, which are feelings, after all, and indeed the best of feelings? That is not enough, of course; far from it. Not all the patience and the integrity in the world can answer this question of François', a writer too—a question that always stuns me : "Is what you are doing now any good?"

Yes, is it good? But what does that mean? And above all, what has it to do with me? Good for what? Good for the readers of today, tomorrow, always? Good for me? For him? What does he expect me to know about it? And if I thought about it, how could I write? To a certain extent, writing is the same as Pascal's wager. Clearly, one can devote as much time, faith and patience to the writing of a bad book as of a good. In all honesty one can make a mistake over subject, means and vocation. A misadventure, a failure, a bad painting, an inadequate book may nevertheless not be without value for the man who experiences them and who seeks for his own truth in them. The bad book is good, for him. Mine may enlighten no one but myself; teach no one but me this labour, this inquiry, and this patience. And yet I acquire, I own, this labour and this research; I know that these corrections, this going back and starting again, even these mistakes have a *relationship* (and this time I use the word designedly) with the mistakes, the questions and the failures that I may meet with in my life: *relationship; not identity.*

A relationship then between myself at the café from half past seven until noon, and myself gossiping with a friend, taking my child or my children for a walk, talking to Luc, seeing an exhibition, suffering from a headache, deciding upon one course of action or another. But what relationship? Once I have spotted this cloud, this link, I want to define it. Myself writing, myself reading, myself responding to the papers, to happenings, to people: the relationship. Myself in Tunisia, for example, which lies in time between innocence and thought, on the confines of awareness. Me, to whom Luc, like M. Jourdain's poetry-master, explains "But you are talking politics," when I had no idea of it. Yes, what is the link between an untopical novel and

myself in Tunisia?

Myself; in no way topical, but going to Tunisia to see my husband (not yet my husband), who was doing his military service there. Anticipation of the meeting: taking ship with a deck ticket

—deck meaning the bottom of the hold with the hatches battened down over my head and the heads of a great many squatting Arabs. Uneventful crossing. In the half-darkness, some way from me, two men fight for quite a while, amidst a general lack of interest.

A venerable patriarch takes me under his protection and doses me with fizzy lemonade when sea-sickness threatens. A woman gives me her baby to hold, and it copiously wets my rucksack. That's all. Tunis. Sun. Luc, who is passing through, asks me to dinner. He had come by plane, and my journey seems more picturesque to him than it does to me. That deck ticket! A hint of distrust shadows his amusement and I think he utters the word 'demagogy'; he speaks to me about the state of affairs in North Africa, which I know nothing at all about.

The sun on the pavements of Tunis. Tomorrow, train to S., my journey's end. Young men go by, overturning the tins in front of the beggars with the ends of their sticks or their feet by way of amusement. The coins spill out. Some are lost. I think this is a bad thing. Luc tells me that "I must not take sides without knowledge." Knowledge of what? I wonder about it.

S. A grey sky with blue, a smooth, faded, worked-over sky, against which there stand out ochre sails, curved like scythes. Tiled floor in the bedroom, cool underfoot; waiting for the evening; the altered smell of a friendly body; smooth gliding along the rediscovered ways. Waiting : walking about the town. Do not go into the Medina alone. All right. Saïd is eleven : sickly, plain. You are not accosted when you walk about with a child. Silently we eat a snack in the square. "When you are back in France you will send me some blue jeans," says Saïd. Yes. I write down his address as he gives it me. Am I in the act of taking sides?

Old women search through dustbins near the barracks. They are given the leavings from the soldiers' canteen. By way of amusing themselves, some of the men throw the leavings some distance instead of putting them in the old rusty cans. Sometimes, not

often, two old women have a silent, joyless fight. Laughter. At
this point it is easy to take sides and to grow indignant. It is not
easy to understand. It is easy to say "bastards" : but why are they
bastards? Why do they find this *funny*? Two women turned into
beasts, rolling in the dust. It might be a Goya print. Even a stupid
peasant must have a certain kind of idea that hunger is not funny.
What is it, then? Delight in evil? Feeling of superiority? When
he is writing phoney news Luc has a feeling of superiority. Debase
the reader. But anyone can be deceived; anyone can be hungry.
Faced with a certain degree of hunger, pain, fear, anyone is going
to lose his dignity and his self-control. It is only the degree that
varies. So where is the superiority in reducing others to that state?
Illusory.

Did I take sides? I merely turned things over in my mind. I
admitted that things had the right to exist and to set me questions: I did not yet find the answers to them. Without too much
sentimentality. Suffering and death did not make me weep: I
accepted nature's law for myself. If I was able to help a sick or
poverty-stricken person, I did. It did not disturb my peace of
mind, for I was myself this sick or poor person and I acquiesced
in this condition; only the operation of chance separated me from
him or brought me nearer. It seemed to me that I was breathing
in harmony with the world. I had never loved without being
loved, never seen love die without feeling its death within myself
as well. I had known and accepted illness: lack of money, such
as I had experienced it, seemed to me trifling compared with certain degrees of wretchedness. I thought of death with pleasure.

This boy's stupid, red-cheeked face, laughing as he threw the
meat the old women longed for a great way off, forced itself
into my mind and pulled me up short. I would never have thought
of requiring him to be pitiful: nature does not know pity. Indifference would have been enough for me. Had I been hungry, old
and infirm (nothing was easier for me than *being* one of those
women; and who can tell but that I was not virtually one of

them?) indifference would have been enough for me—I should have agreed to that state of affairs. But the laugh? Was he not taking sides? I put that face away for reference. I was to return to it.

The children begged. We gave them what we could, and presently we were being followed by a crowd of urchins, half begging, half playing. They amused themselves as we went along, and only one or two remained with us—perhaps a brother and sister. Giving in, we were going to let them have a last little coin when a man who had been watching them asking for money suddenly came forward, threatening them violently with words and gestures. They ran away.

The man was not a *colon*, not a European. He was an Arab and he was humiliated. I could understand both that and his painful anger. Humiliation is not a complicated feeling. Understand it. Luc: "Politics has nothing to do with sentiment. You must see things as they really are. When it was not we who were oppressing these people it was the tribal chiefs." Historical development. I turned it over in my mind. Surely the fact that things are as they really are should not stop one from defining them as wrong? Or from trying to make them better? I am quite aware of the elementary, even childish, nature of these reflections. Luc is aware of it too, and tells me so. "But why do you insist on talking politics when you know nothing about them?"

"But I don't *want* to talk politics. I happen to be here and I have noticed certain things, and I have thought about them . . ."

"Why think about them?"

"Why not?"

"You ought not to interfere. You don't know anything about these things and yet you take sides . . ."

He goes off cross, leaving me confronted with this obvious fact: *to reflect is already to take sides*. The Boss's ideas, exactly. Exactly along the same line that has made the word 'intellectual' an insult. I wonder whether I am becoming an intellectual. A diffi-

cult conversion. It seems to me that I have neither the good qualities nor the defects. Young right-wing men and their studied
off-handedness; young left-wing women and their simple-minded
progressivism : I feel that I am as far from the one as the other.
Art, politics, feeling : I was not inclined to go into these ideas,
these qualifications.

More and more the figure of the Boss assumed a revealing
importance in my eyes, swelling to the scale of the universe,
becoming a kind of Moloch, a god in an American film, made
of gilt cardboard to look like gold or bronze, a ghastly Chinese-
Mexican confusion, but one which belches fire and terrorizes the
wretched crowd of supers at two dollars an hour who mime their
own slavish state in nylon peplums. Moloch or sphinx with the
everlasting motto, full of significance in its brevity : "I do not
want to know."

I did want to know. What, what about, and how? Everything
had to be recast. But the Boss showed me the world as it was—
an essential step. By making up my mind to turn things over, to
think, I quitted a magic circle. But I could only have stayed in
it by taking the opposite decision, the Boss's decision : "I do not
want to know." And if I had thought that I could take shelter
there, I should still have left the enchanted regions where no
questions ever arise.

I reached the point of asking myself "Do these regions exist
at all?" Once one *thinks,* however blunderingly, however
scrappily, one finds out that one has always *thought.*

A thousand childhood memories come alive again. One has
always thought. And it is not without a certain sadness that one
becomes aware of this : just as after a break that would have
seemed unbelievable a week before, a lover may suddenly become
aware of a thousand little facts that were overlain at the moment
but, since they reappear, were not forgotten, and which in the
past would have shown him (if he had chosen to take notice of
them) that already things were not as they might be, whereas he

still believed, wanted to believe, that he was in the midst of happiness. He too "did not *want* to know."

Yet this desire for ignorance may reach the point of sublimity and may become the laying of a bet on goodness, which is that charity that "believes all, hopes all, bears all," that is not blindness, not silliness, but that is quite certainly taking sides, a wager on goodness, a laying of everything one possesses on love. And that has a relationship (but only a relationship) with that wager on art that one makes when one writes. How is this to be resolved?

Wager on art. Working in the dark, which makes the question "is it good?" distressing and pointless. Relationship of this bet with love; and with politics—why not?

Is not asserting that although things "are what they are" one must not consent to their being so, and knowing that every alteration must in its turn alter—is not this bearing all and at the same time hoping all? Just as writing is—writing without ever reaching the goal that one has set oneself, bearing the distress and always beginning to write again?

No, it is not *the same thing*. Related, not identical. It has often been pointed out (and not without glee) that the writer of some fine book, the upholder of some noble cause, the originator of a new science, was not necessarily a 'good' man. It has been said so often that some people have thought it quite essential not to be upright 'in life' so that they might be 'in art'. Not all drunkards are Verlaine, not all homosexuals Garcia Lorca; not all gallows-birds are Rimbaud or Genet. Yet the kind of South Sea island superstition, according to which people believe they can take on the virtues of a great man by adopting his vices, is very usual. Pitiful mimicry.

On the other hand, in spite of Daniel d'Arthez (perhaps the only character that Balzac ever failed to bring off) patience and length of time are not enough to produce a great work either, although they do help. When a great man has, in some respects, a little soul, I attribute it above all to want of logic. In a word, to inadvertence. "He hasn't made the connexion", as they say. For the moment I shall call this connexion

courage

Cézanne at Aix, towards the end of his life. That is a subject that tempts me. Twenty-four hours of his life, in which nothing happens. Or perhaps a fortnight, from the beginning of a picture to the end of it. He has a letter from his son, he thinks about Zola, he bitterly regrets not having been accepted for the Salon, not having been given the *Légion d'honneur*. He is filled with doubt and he destroys a canvas; yet he does not doubt, either, for he begins again, and knows that he will go on beginning again until he dies. He knows that a truth exists. Or, not to be presumptuous, let us say he believes that a truth exists.

What I find so attractive is that temperate, measured curse. Not at all Gauguin's appalling (and somewhat too showy) end, that rather high-flown set piece. It is too typical altogether, like his desertion of wife and children—a stock image for the horrified, delighted bourgeois. You may say that Gauguin paid very heavily for that self-satisfaction, that very slight trace of self-satisfaction, which he may have had about his own highly-coloured, strong-smelling misfortunes (but a single fly in a whole pot of ointment . . .).

He paid for his 'life of an artist' with his gangrened flesh, his utter forlornness, his painful knowledge of the leaky huts of Tahiti, so much less poetic when one lives in them than when one sees them from a distance. No doubt all that is true. Yet although that smell, that very faint smell, that decorative smell with its whiff of the strip cartoon which instantly charms the readers of *France-Soir,* is quite redeemed, I find it as repulsive as the smell of a corpse.

But the sadness of the man who longs ingenuously for the honours of this world and who finds that because of a certain truth in him which he is utterly obliged to express ("that little feeling", he said; as Corot, who managed these things better for himself, called his finest pictures—those he never showed— "my flights of fancy"), these honours are refused him: Cézanne's sadness, which you may describe as bourgeois if you like, and Manet's innocent stupefaction at the uproar caused by his Olympia, and the way in which they were nevertheless obliged to go on painting more *Mont Sainte-Victoires*, more *Déjeuners sur l'herbe*—there is a real human fate, a real human standard, a real human sadness, with no display, no tragic trimmings.

And that continual misunderstanding of everyday life together with all this, these eyes so preoccupied with one truth that they no longer see the others—Cézanne looking at Van Gogh's canvasses and crying "This is the painting of a lunatic!": Zola, that generous heart, stuffing his Cézannes away in the attic while Bonnats held pride of place in his *mediaeval* drawing-room: and Cézanne hearing of the generous, *true* role played by Zola in the Dreyfus affair (that part which he had so much merit in playing because he was afraid of it—again a human standard. The very slightest self-satisfaction at the 'star part' aspect of his stepping in would have spoilt everything)—Cézanne observing, with a sigh, "Poor old Emile: he has let himself get entangled again . . ."

Yes, I only like the 'curse of genius' when it is suffered unwillingly. I do not care for it when it is sought out and worn as a becoming garment. The same applies to innovation in form and style: I only like them when they stem from a strong necessity of mind, when they are not even conscious of being new and are quite taken aback at attracting so much notice, having been so sure that they were natural. When an innovation is self-conscious, full of theory, setting itself up as a rule, it irks me in the same way as Brummel's new coat, a Sunday suit or the dubbing of a Western. "Are you coming, Betty? Give me my Colt," in French has (to my ears) the same affected sound, and it ends up by being merely funny. It seems to me that the coat feels rather too strongly that it *is* Brummel—the perpetual fetish. And if I like a man to struggle against the truth a little, it is because the force of the truth breaks out all the stronger for it. I love the truth. So I believe that there is one. That, at least, is something settled.

And I love Cézanne at Aix: painting, but without material worries; burdened with an indifferent wife, but having an affectionate son; no longer being able to believe that he will win the admiration or the understanding of others, but always retaining faith in himself; no longer understanding his friend Zola, who no longer understands him, but understanding the speech of the mountains for all eternity. I prefer a modest (and not so very modest) struggle to an immense self-conscious unhappiness. Cézanne was a man. Gauguin,

a stock figure

Apart from Vincent Van Gogh there has been hardly anyone who has been a stock figure without paying for it. There was Van Gogh, yes: so there are miracles in which the corniest old worn-out cliché takes on life and passion again through being lived with total innocence. But there has been scarcely anyone other than Van Gogh to preserve the stock figure of 'the great artist consumed by his art' and struck down at high noon. Not that I am entirely against stock figures. Some of them are really charming—twopenny coloured pictures.

Take Einstein, for example. There is a stock figure that always pleases everybody—the world-famous scientist who found it so hard to get across the road without being run over. The dream of specialization can hardly go farther, can it? (And the dear unworldly face gave less pleasure when he wanted to intervene in what was at once called 'politics'. Each man to his own trade and the atomic bombs will soon be dealt with.) Another genuinely picturesque figure—Jean Rostand and his frogs. A figure for people of a certain cultural level, of course. Not everyone is satisfied with Margaret or the Persian baby. Indeed, it may even be said that in some circles these stock figures are looked upon with the same scorn as the grocer's calendar. And yet . . .

A fellow-novelist, a friend, cultivated, percipient, helpful, perfect, said, "I will introduce So-and-so to you; he is an extraordinary *character*." For him, of course, Margaret is not a character. He has too delicate a stomach for that kind of cooking. Ah, but on the other hand I do suspect him of having a certain conscious bad taste that is the height of a particular kind of good taste (no, he is *not in the least* homosexual)—a taste for the green uniform and the splendours of the Académie française, just as one has a liking for Victorian furniture and that romantic print of a thin-faced girl swinging under an equally thin-faced period moon.

The picturesque : a sure-fire effect for the lovers of Balzac, old Paris, the flea-market, the ragged eccentrics who raise a canary (and who dream of a roast chicken, while they are photographed). You will say, "What, are *you* saying unkind things about Balzac, you who . . ." But Balzac is the saviour of the picturesque, as Van Gogh is the saviour of the curse of art. And then Balzac is perpetually struggling with the demon Bric-à-brac, and he does not always win. But at least he never gives in, and his victory is all the finer for having been so fought for.

But you have to be very strong to venture upon this fight with the picturesque, very strong not to go under. The horrible auction-room picturesque, the horrible demon of inventories, and the horrible demon of exoticism; and the no less horrible counterpart demon, the distinguished pure-psychology-fancier, a Prince de Clèves in his forties sitting in Fouquet's with a glass of whiskey in his hand, elegantly non-existent like all demons—a demon who will vanish (in smoke) if you ask him what he lives on . . .

The horrible demon of specialization, the prince of characters and theories! One might compose litanies about him that would make Baudelaire tremble. And yet how many allies this devil does draw to himself, how many tourists delighted by the winding of these picturesque alleys. And yet I am speaking only of the artistic tourists, not of those who go off on holiday, on vacation (what a lovely word that is, when you think of it: vacation, emptying of heart and mind; vacant, empty, cameras for recording pictures that have been catalogued beforehand, the camera slung, the eye the captive of the lens), and look at the life of others and believe they have understood it. But is it possible that we—you, reader, and you, my writing friends—should still be so near to our childhood, setting up our imagination like a screen, like a Punch and Judy show among the trees that we do not see, making *characters* pass across the stage?

"He is a fine character . . . This odd character . . . The chief characters . . ." So right away we are told that we are at a show, that there is nothing to be afraid of, and that (even if there is suffering and death in the gaudy scenery) it is 'all in fun' . . . "It is odd, but the funny part does not make me laugh," said Daniel when he was five. He loathed the circus. The clowns made him cry. It seemed to him that so much ugliness was a cause for pity rather than laughter. He was shown that it was nothing more than dressing up and flour and rouge on their faces, and that these men had only to wash to look as ordinary as the people watching them. "Then why don't they wash at once?" asked Daniel, for whom it was inconceivable that anyone should take pleasure in being laughed at. "Because that is how they earn their living." "So there you are—it *is* very sad," he said.

Most probably Daniel is not an 'artist'. He is not entirely right either. But his horror of the clown proves that the clown is not only a character without solidity, without relation (yes, indeed) to anything at all. Our laughing at this monster gives us our revenge for having been frightened by other monsters. May it be that these characters whom one shuts away in themselves, whom one isolates, excuse one from really looking at them? But what is an extraordinary character?

In 1900 an extraordinary character was a White Russian, once a grand-duke and now a seller of pancakes in the Place Pigalle, a person with a profound regard for icons, some very strange superstitions, patent-leather shoes and no socks. It was a learned, unwashed revolutionary; it was (oh Arsène Lupin!) a fashionable swindler: in short, a *social contrast*. Nowadays the contrast is psychological rather: no doubt it may still be one of King Farouk's dignitaries, who owned three yachts and a gold-mine and who has now become a painter of children's model cars, the owner of no more gold than what is in his teeth.

But it may also be a supremely elegant woman of the highest society who is said to lie with her dog and who retorts "How can you be so absurd? It is not dogs at all, but monkeys." It may be a homosexual lover of painting, an erotomaniac who collects shoes, a girl of the sophisticated world who is a virgin, a hetero-sexual swashbuckler or a willowy smuggler of gold. It may be the owner of a scandal-sheet who sheds tears as he listens to Darius Milhaud.

Speaking of his chief Luc says, "Truth does not exist for him: he is an extraordinary character." And speaking of a mercenary Lambert says, "He passed the time shooting the natives who were swimming in the river, and he said 'I am so fond of crocodiles'. He is an extraordinary character." A run-of-the-mill extra-ordinary character would be a former Carmelite nun turned strip-tease dancer (delicate stomachs keep out). Gauguin: there is a splendid example—a delight to one and all. The bourgeois will be particularly pleased with the curse, the 'agony among the tropical greenery' angle (and there is this word *angle*—it became common about the middle of the war, didn't it? People and things are not only divided into categories but now they also have to be subdivided into *angles*!!!)—the stage agony angle, as I was saying.

The sophisticated will prefer this letter: "I leave my children to the mercy of the winds . . ." and will contrast this good-natured

effrontery with Rousseau's delicate hypocrisy (my children will
be better brought up by the state than by me). Extraordinary,
indeed. One is so taken up with staring that one forgets the
little straws of children, who have in fact vanished down the
wind. And Sade? A very old line of goods, but always in demand.
And Lautréament? Pretty pictures for belated surrealists and New
Wave left-wingers.

And Jean Genet! One feels like thanking him for matching
the myth of literary sanctity so perfectly. The only possible
objection is that he might be a little more obscure. But apart
from that, quite perfect : not another touch is wanted. Sodomy,
criminal record, lyricism and anarchy. There is an extraordinary
character, if I know anything at all about it. There is hardly anyone but Verlaine who deals out such good measure and who gives
the customers such thorough satisfaction.

There was only one blot on Verlaine's life, and that was its
end. Everything had been got ready—articles, photos, prints :
it was already in the primers . . . and yet he did not die in the
workhouse. There was nothing to be done about it. He "died
at the house of a fellow-countrywoman, Mme X, who had taken
him in during his illness." Universal indignation. See the papers
of the time. The image of the Pauvre Lélian, the Swan of
Cambrai, the Singer of Nuremberg! The countless people who
call Rousseau 'Jean-Jacques' and the great many who say 'Jean'
for Jean Cocteau! And those too who call Bobet 'Louison' and
Gaul 'Charly' . . . And (shocking though it is to say) those who
invented the nickname of Plum Pudding for Prince Charles of
England. And (enough to make one weep into one's handkerchief
over the 'green Paradise') that childhood friend who writes to me
after years of silence and begins her letter thus—"Well, Madame
Fémina?")

Let us hide our heads, for we are all guilty; let us cover ourselves with ashes, for we all sin, all of us, from the bar-keeper who
states, "*All* Germans are honest : it is their only virtue", to the

journalist who *deeply regrets* that the dwelling of Mme X, Verlaine's countrywoman, should have been "prettily decked with flowers". We want pictures, characters and strong colours, or else let us have our money back! It is not funny any more! We insist upon the fatal end and the workhouse. Since it is 'all in fun' we insist that it should be funny.

The workhouse! The workhouse for 'extraordinary characters'! A little servant says, "It's a shame, Margaret getting married. She was so much better unhappy." Just as you might say that Bardot was better "as an ingénue," or Marilyn "as a vamp." Margaret to the workhouse! It is much more photogenic. The image-fancier insists upon it. He does not like Cézanne, Manet is a bourgeois, Degas an ill-tempered aristocrat, even Delacroix and his darkness is not dramatic enough—he wants the virgin forest, the reek of gangrene, and delirium—it is unthinkable that Gauguin should not have been delirious. And he must die of it! Like Rimbaud! Because after all, suppose that Rimbaud had not died, that he had simply made his fortune, that he had married and begotten little Rimbauds, how many thesis-writers and commentators would be out of a job! "You can't make anything of it all," as the *Paris-Match* photographers put it.

Even Baudelaire has never managed to come up to Rimbaud as a stock figure in popular aesthetics, although indeed he did his best, with his Oedipus complexes galore, his hatred for generals, voluntary damnation, Satan, black mistresses, opium and, to cap it all, his pox. It was enough that once, just once, the poor soul should have made the resolution (which he never kept) to get up early in the morning and to work regularly : that was enough, and M. Sartre will never forgive him for it. It was no good *his* dying, genuinely dying, in the workhouse; it was too late, and he could not atone for the error of having said his prayers once or twice and having drunk a glass or so less. This kind of thing, says M. Sartre, is no joking matter.

And the public is behind him. However much one touches it

up, blackens it, sets it off to advantage, Baudelaire's fate still looks too human. It has a whiff of real suffering, and real suffering is disagreeable to well-bred noses. Whereas Rimbaud is the perfect, ineffable myth. And our image-mongers, all dons at heart, both the Christians and the rebels, stew their brains over this splendid subject for a treatise. Rimbaud is the ideal subject for lovers of Eden, of fatalism, of "the spirit bloweth where it listeth." Some Christians with strong digestions manage to get it down; but it is Quietism—Mme Guyon swallowing the gobs of phlegm. They have to swallow too hard to savour it properly. The man who has not lived his life to the end. Not lived his genius—or the exhaustion of his genius—to the end. The grandeur of this self-murder, they will say.

I do not like suicides. It seems to me that there is more grandeur in looking at oneself as one is than in running away from oneself by jumping out of the window. More grandeur in taking up one's suffering, one's importance as a creator, than in escaping from it. Pity, certainly, as much as you like; and understanding—it is understandable that a sick man in intolerable pain should fling himself upon any kind of drug. He cannot bear any more, he has come to the end of his strength, eaten up by his own genius, like Van Gogh, who had a precariously balanced mind, or Modigliani, who had a receding chin.

Tragedy, yes, a hundred times. But grandeur? Merit? Where is the merit in having a cancer and dying of it? That is how a destiny, a fate, is mucked about to make a 'character' out of it. I infinitely prefer the original article. My theme could be a destiny —but that would be rather too easy. I should be afraid of calling up that silly admiration that wallows in grandiose disasters and deathless tears. My theme—the theme that I dream of—is Cézanne at Aix, alone with himself; Cézanne knowing that he will begin this day's work again and again until his days come to an end. My theme is courage. And courage is not a speciality.

I am quite aware that this theme runs the risk of seeming rather limited. I know that it is rather naked and rather laid out flat, and even that it does not appear to leave room for inspiration (however out-of-date that word may be), for poetry, or for beauty. Only in the matter of beauty there is nothing that I can do except wait for it and yield to it. My history is the history of this waiting; my inquiry that of this courage. How can one presume to speak of what remains? In the long run I shall certainly come, if not to knowing what I want, then at least to knowing what I want to know.

I am only just coming out of the limbo of a long childhood. I am coming out of it thanks to these books, which serve as a road for me, and which, for me, are good. It may be that this road can be seen by others and that it may be possible to communicate my research. And in that case I suppose that these will be what are called *good books*. It may be that they are so only for me. Yes. That may be.

Communicate with others. Just talk to other people. There is already a great deal of ambition in that. I am beginning to want to communicate with myself, to coincide with myself. I feel that there is some relationship between the morning me and the evening me, and that it would be useful for me to decide the nature of this relationship, and if possible to control it. If I were to know what I might call the raw material at my disposal, I could then tell how best to make use of it, without letting myself be blindly led by it, and yet without claiming to alter anything of its essence either.

So think. Write. Think in a scrappy, desultory manner, with merely the help of the little facts of daily life, since, I said to myself, that was all I had at my service . . . This was not unconnected with my first collector's delight in discovering words and their relationship with things, in meeting some particular image or feeling during the course of the day—those bricks carried to my little personal building: but more and more I felt the need that this building, far from being *mine*, as I had thought, should make part of a universal construction, towards the building of which each helps according to his ability and (this time I liked the word) according to his speciality.

Having been in my absurd and necessary place in an absurd and innocent world, I wanted to rediscover the natural order, and find a definite place in a world that meant something. Meant what, though? Everything had to be begun again from the beginning. This did not distress me. In the absence of other qualities, I did have that of patience, attentive care.

The beginning was *art*—these words, these phrases, this childish delight (stemming from Eden in the first place), this given, free delight, as it seemed to me. The 'artist' of the magazines, the absent-minded scientist, the extraordinary character with whom one has nothing to do or who does not have to do anything : the beginning was that entranced, entrancing collector of pebbles, the postman Cheval building his Palais Idéal and writing this pretty quatrain on his wheelbarrow—

> In me you see the helper kind,
> The thoughtful worker's constant mate,
> Who daily in the fields would find
> His little share proportionate.

Do not misunderstand me. I am entirely for the postman Cheval, and I have been these many years. They say that he began by bringing the stones he used for building his palace back in his handkerchief. His wife complained, because of the wear on the cloth. So he took to using a wheelbarrow. He wandered forth in the twilight, picking out the most beautiful stones, abandoning this polished pebble in favour of that spotted one, planning giants, archways and also poems to write on the ground; and I like to think that he was happy, while Mme Cheval sat moping at home.

Peace-loving, persevering postman Cheval, you who have built this Palais Idéal at Hauterives (Drôme), you deserve to be applauded, you deserve to be congratulated, postman Cheval, the laughing-stock of your village, the butt of your wife. (Or was she on the contrary a helpmeet to you? Did she end up by being won over by your zeal, and by proudly bringing her contribution to your 'little share' of stones?) Patience, steadiness and modesty: those are your virtues, postman Cheval. We love them; your palace delights us, and by your guileless verses we are almost moved to tears.

> Seeking I found:
> Forty years have I laboured
> To bring from the ground
> This fairy-tale palace.

What moral teaching there is in the distich cut into the west front (crenellated, and ornamented with a false palm-tree made of stone): "To the courageous heart, nothing is impossible". How much modest pride on the north façade (representing a Hindu temple overlaid with stalactites and hollowed into mysterious grottoes): "A benevolent spirit drew me from the void." And decorating 'The Queen of the Grottoes' there is an inscription with a social aim: "All that thou seest, passer by, is the work of a peasant's hand". And lastly on the Barbary Tower (what a beautiful name) here is the summing-up of this life-time's work:

> I wanted to prove, by building this tower,
> The strength of the mind, its height and its power.

It can do a great deal, strength of mind, postman Cheval. It can create a Palais Idéal; spanning the years it can draw our sympathy towards you and our esteem: and this strength of mind, this will, must have turned your life into an absorbing task, civilizing your manners and developing your imagination and your muscles. It has shown us what the Palais Idéal of a postman

Cheval really is; and that is fascinating. It may inspire all sorts of reflexions in us; and of course it has turned you into a fine 'extraordinary character'. It has not been able to turn your Palais into a work of art.

Why not? Were you not gifted enough, postman Cheval? Was it your culture that was inadequate? Were you really less cultivated than Cézanne, who was interested in nothing but himself, or than Rodin, who could scarcely read? How does it come about that you stayed on the edge, in the picturesque and the unexpected, that region that borders upon art, without ever being able to cross the frontier?

You had patience and steadiness of purpose, and modesty; you had dexterity and imagination—that is proved by your two giants, which might very nearly have been conceived by Paul Klee. Your taste for your stones and your patient searching was like ours when, day after day, we heaped up and wheeled off our own feelings just as you did with your biggest stones "to make something of them." And I do not believe that we were more gifted than you, postman Cheval: you were quite skilful, since you expressed exactly what you wanted to express. The fact, postman Cheval, that we may have been more cultivated than you, more provided with all sorts of points of contact, only stood in our way, blinding us as to our true choice when we went in search of "our little share".

In reality we were just like you. And we still should be, if we had kept our noses down to our pebbles, postman Cheval, however shining and mottled and like our childhood dreams they may have been. What saved us (or, as some will say, destroyed us) was suddenly raising our heads, looking into the night and opening ourselves to it; and asking ourselves, perhaps, why we were there.

Afterwards we returned to our wheelbarrow, since the wheelbarrow was our particular tool. But in our Palais Idéal we did try to leave a space for the night.

pebbles

The other day my friend René came to see me. He is a novelist; indeed, a good novelist. He chooses his pebbles with taste, and he gives up all his free moments to his writing, for he has another job at which he works bravely so as to feed his children and a wife who, like Mme Cheval, sighs proudly and bitterly at his toil-filled evenings. René has postman Cheval's blue, innocent, guileless and somewhat short-sighted gaze, and his total sincerity. He busies himself about his Palais Idéal with a truly praiseworthy zeal. He ought to succeed, as they say. "To the courageous heart, nothing is impossible." René turns up one morning, dreadfully upset, with tears standing in his short-sighted eyes.

"What am I to do? My mistress is pregnant!"

I am amazed. René, a mistress . . . Yet he is no sort of a man to waste valuable time in empty affairs, nor to abandon the search for stones for that of butterflies. What is more, I know that he is a methodical creature and that he has just begun to have his flat redecorated : it would be quite out of character for him to commit himself to expense in two directions at once.

"Have you got a mistress?"

"No," says he, with a movement of disgust. "That is . . . I will tell you all about it . . ." (He settles down in a chair. His mild, unworldly face bears the mark of suffering innocence unjustly punished.) "It is not in the least that I have a mistress. You know me and you know how I adore Marthe and the children; I am having the place redecorated, and I would never have gone . . ."

"That is exactly what I was thinking."

". . . have gone and found a mistress at this point. But there is my novel."

"Eh? Your . . ."

"Yes. I wanted to write about the life of one of those girls who . . . whom . . . Jacqueline was exactly the type of girl I meant. Way of thinking, way of speaking, even her way of dressing—

there are some things you just can't invent: you know that. I took her out—it was perfectly natural—and in the cinema, do you see . . . Absolutely my character, you understand. So . . ."

I understood. 'Jacqueline' was no longer a woman for him, Marthe's rival, a danger for his dear children, but a PEBBLE, miraculously discovered within hand's reach just as he was labouring away, unable to turn his eyes from the gap in his building, the gaping hole that absolutely had to be filled: under the pressure of necessity she had turned into that indispensable thing, a stone. Astonishing discovery—René was a postman Cheval! Had I not been one myself? Yet that had been the beginning of 'art' for me.

As far back as I can remember, that is to say, about the time when I was twelve, for me the need to write has been the same as the need to make things last, to preserve them. When I was twelve or thereabouts my mother and I went into the country for a few days; I made a little book out of this, a kind of humorous (!) novel called *The Journey to Beersel*. Before that I had filled one or two exercise-books with fantasies—tales in the Jules Verne manner, stories about divers. But they had never given me the same satisfaction as this 'true to life novel'. The feeling that this journey had 'served a purpose', although it was over, that it had had a second existence, this time definitive, that there were 'directions for use' for life and a way of losing nothing—all this gave me for the first time a feeling of safety and a peace that I was to find over a long space of years in the act of writing, and only in the act of writing.

And indeed there is a great pleasure and a great tranquillity in reflecting that while the days and their events flit by, a wealth is heaping up inside you, without your knowing it, as it were, almost automatically, and that one day when you choose you will only have to turn to this wealth and quietly make use of it. That these human beings, rooms, landscapes, however lovely they may be, however moving, do not die fleeting away, but join together, counterbalance one another, rising up in tiers.

Nothing is useless any more. So the passing of time no longer causes distress but rather the delight of ownership since lost time is, on the contrary, for ever won. The Palais Idéal is built from the pebbles on the road. Tiredness is forgotten. (It forgets itself—does not consent to exist. I shall come back to this. And to that other peace, which consists of accepting the fact that the book too is transient, that it too passes . . .)

So I quite understand René's manner of working and his pleasure in it. Yet the idea of manufacturing events so as to make use of them had never occurred to me. I was satisfied with what time brought me; I despised nothing, and what I did not use I put to one side; but I never had the idea of stirring up these materials, of building cloud-palaces, of taking part in a kind of play that I should act to myself and that I should copy afterwards. I asked René for more details. It seemed curious to me.

"Did you never love her?"

"Oh, never!" he cried, indignantly.

"Desire perhaps . . ."

"Not at all! As I told you, I was only thinking of my book. I just happened to run into this wench and I said to myself 'This is exactly the character I need.' I asked her out, and . . ."

"And you fell?"

"I felt that she would only reveal herself entirely to a man who . . ." he said, thoughtfully. "Women, you know . . ."

"And she is pregnant."

His face grew distracted again.

"Yes. Would you believe it? What a ghastly thing! And Marthe and the children, and . . ."

"The redecoration; I know. And you are quite sure that it is you . . ."

His mild un-human face at once became more earthly. For a moment a shadow of complacency clouded his shining simplicity.

"Oh, she adores me," he said.

Let me reassure the tender reader at once. René's mistress was not pregnant, and though she 'adored him' she consoled herself when he absent-mindedly broke with her after his proofs had come in. I say that she consoled herself for the loss of René. Did she console herself quite so easily when, running through those brand-new pages, she found that she had been only a pebble? I do not know. It may be that she takes greater pleasure in being herself, in looking at herself in the mirror. And that in the evening, when she is very old, by candlelight . . .

Yes. All the same, if one day she gets a hint of the way her adventure was planned, of the stop-gap role, defined beforehand, to which she was assigned and beyond which she could not go— not the least chance, whatever she said or did; if she realizes that when she was pouring herself out in high-flown silliness on the stage of that little theatre in which René was for the moment the entire audience, she was not improvising, not surprising anyone, not, in total freedom, creating a play which might (by chance) have *inspired* a book, but that she was acting out (and perhaps suffering from an unrewarding narrow part or from too deep a range of voice or from having things to say that were either too learned or too simple-minded for her) this book that had *already been written*, this prefabricated adventure.

That she was the victim of something that was bound to happen, a department store fatality, a fatality under the imprint of a popular publisher, a 595 franc fatality if the part was thin, cut to the essentials and reduced to 160 pages in royal octavo.

Or else reaching as high as 1,200 francs (twelve new francs) if it was really carried out right to the end and if it was filled with realistic sediment, little things known to her alone, but carefully *slanted* : for from the beginning it had been determined that her mother's name should be Stéphanie and that they should go to eat at the Dupont Latin with her wearing a pink blouse, a blouse of a particular sickening pink, the pink of guts and of a kiss and of a little girl's ribbon, symbolizing in turn disgust, surfeit and then (just before the *already described, already wept-over, already experienced* break) once more representing, in a last flare-up of pity and desire, her childhood, innocence and ignorance (she really possessed them, and they were hers in René's book).

If she could be aware of all this, if she had no more than a hint of it, would she not suddenly experience the shock, the humiliation, of a woman who knows that she is not beautiful and who is surprised in her bath—that woman cut off from her body, which is suddenly judged and perfidiously condemned while it was trustfully letting itself go in the lapping warmth, supposing that it was still free to have no meaning . . .

It is not my way to judge my friends. What shocked me in René's adventure was neither his unfaithfulness nor his rashness nor even the offhand way in which he broke it off : it was the lack of freedom in the whole thing. Or the lack of inspiration, if you would rather. That mild executioner's face seemed all the more disturbing to me in that it was not cruel—that it thought of itself as urged on by an imperative need. That it called this need into being. It was no longer even a question of making use of time, life and chance, but of mutilating them, of being a foregone conclusion to oneself and to others. As nothing could alter René's novel, which was determined from as early as the first page, so nothing could change the course of his prefabricated love-affair.

In short, I was shocked by the fact that he had not allowed Jacqueline (nor the Jacqueline of the novel, for that matter) the least chance of living with a life of her own. Which is rendered in all the melodramas in the world by the sweet phrase, "You have used me as a plaything!" And yet that is not right. There is an implicit contract between the plaything and the player : the child who makes a doll of a spoon does not thereby entirely deny the spoon's existence; the child knows (and the delight of the playing lies in this ambiguity) that the doll is also a spoon. That is the ambiguity of half-love, and it gives it a sacrilegious charm.

No, the word toy is still too loose for René's loves, René's books. *Accessory* seems more exact to me. You use an accessory for a

perfectly distinct purpose and you put it down again without even
looking at it. "The object of his love" is also a fine, enriching
thing to say; like "the subject of your book." "What is it about?"
they say. And heavily, working hard, the author replies, "Well,
it's . . . [a long pause] . . . it's about a very wealthy old gentleman
who . . ."

It is about. Everybody is reassured. It has no relationship with
anything. It is thoroughly shut away, thoroughly apart; it is literature, it is love and it affects only the writer or the lover, and they,
without anything coming of it, can parade any image they choose,
call for any delight that comes to their mind, without anyone at
all interfering in this world that I should call, if I dared,

the brothel within

The word may seem a little coarse. And yet without wishing to
exaggerate in the very least, it might be said that many love affairs
and some of the most poetic, are brothel-loves. Alex is very fond
of strange deviations and monstrosities, and he tells me that the
well-known cinema director X can only make love with women
harnessed like horses and galloping round and round his flat.
Otherwise, apart from the harness, any woman at all of tolerable
appearance and age will do. Curious image. And how ridiculous
and almost poetic vice appears to those who do not share it!

The harnessed woman makes me think of some of those Persian
miniatures in which the tender brown free-flowing curve of a girl's
flank does indeed bring to mind the splendid arching of a horse;
and the legends of vixen-women, of women turned into hinds, at
once provide me with a horse-woman with red harness against a
grey background, a kind of sphinx that I see as having wings,
jewels in her mane, cloud-high, her hooves barely touching the
shining domes and gleaming minarets.

Alas, sphinxes fly only in our imagination: one comes heavily
back to earth when one learns that the sphinx (who may bear a
vaccination-mark on her arm and a fold of fat on her thigh by

way of showing that she really is of this world) charges a hundred new francs for galloping in flats. Poor breathless conjured-up spirit, who goes back, after this dubious pantomime, to peel potatoes in a cracked sink: does an imagination with any kind of range need her? When there are women who require no more than long eyes slanting up towards their temples, a faint smile and their dark hair wind-blown, to look far more sphinx-like than any sphinx?

But does one grow enamoured even of beautiful hair, a smile, an enigmatic eye, without a little artificiality coming into the emotion? For the poet takes his flight above the minarets, the domes and the white cities with the lovely mask held in his hands, while a face that has no magic in it waits in vain for a glance. And yet whatever he may suppose, the man who makes game of the poet does not really have the best of it: he too is wanting in inspiration. Out of dislike for one despotism he becomes the prisoner of another—one quite without charm. The two faces must be reconciled: one must admit that the one (whichever it may be) is the shadow of the other; and although one cannot look in two directions at once, one ought nevertheless to feel that the one is the complement of the other—one ought to feel this, as one waits for the impossible integration.

Impossible yet always close at hand. The moment at which Vincent Van Gogh, standing between his destiny and his freedom, between the madness that hung over him and the overstretched force of will that made use of it, making it part of the whole, dies of it, as though he were struck down at high noon in that state in which total despair joins total happiness and melts into it, in which the two faces at last recognize one another, accept one another and merge together in what is called

death

Death, because that is the moment when the fighting stops. Death, harmony: a contradictory pair, and yet inseparable. One is afraid of death; and one fights to reach the point at which doubt, uncertainty and anxiety die. One is afraid of death; and one seeks sleep. One is afraid of death, but one is still more afraid of life.

Am I afraid of death? Do I even really believe in it?

Four times already in child-bed, I have believed in death. And during the two or three days after the shock of giving birth I have gone on believing in it; and I can still recover the particular taste of that anguish, of the chasm ready to open in front of me, not very deeply over-laid by the glaze of passing time.

It is said that some women love the babies they carry within them. There are some who lie down on the delivery-bed with a smile of happiness. As far as I am concerned, there is no other name than death for that slow devouring growth of the baby that eats the flesh, the strength and the intelligence of the woman who carries it, as a cancer might eat her life. The very tranquillity that I feel when I am with child, which makes me glide over the thousand little irritations and worries that ordinarily vex me beyond measure, is the proud tranquillity of the condemned.

Nothing exists any more except this term, this inescapable date, *which I cannot alter in any way whatsoever*: above all, nothing exists other than the moment when I shall feel that little hard skull (not then my baby's but rather that of a kind of evil skeleton, an inimical force, against which I can do nothing) moved by an implacable strength of its own, wanting to force a passage for itself, and forcing it while in a desperate effort to cling to life I am obliged to help it, and when I thrust it out with horror and loathing, all covered with wet, clinging shreds of my body, at last set free.

Let them carry it away, rid me of it, and let me rest at last! For two days I have to take sleeping-pills and forget, forget with all my strength. On the third day I can at last meet the wandering blue gaze of my last baby, beside me, that dear little girl for whom I would 'give my life' as they say (and I would too).

Where does this horror come from? For I am not afraid of death. I quite agree that life should have an end, and I even wish that this should be so. It seems to me better arranged like that. Sometimes I ask myself, as one asks oneself "Is my hair all right?" (quite as often—indeed more often), "Would I be ready to die at this moment?" and when I can answer yes I feel a perfectly tranquil satisfaction. With my whole will I consent to death. Well then? Whence the horror of that moment—a happy moment for many women—when the child of my womb makes its stubborn thrust through me towards life?

The horror of the memory of your birth, blue-eyed Vincent with your black eyelashes, whose six years fill me with wonder every day—the miracle that ranges from the 'slightly raised upper lip' of Tolstoy's Princess Lisa to those wonderful drawings that spring from a casually-handled pencil. What relationship is there between the miracle of these two, four, six, thirteen years, this silky hair, this awkwardness filled with grace, this ink everywhere, this tangle of little slippery bodies in the old bath-tub, and that body arched with long torment and that shout that to my astonishment I heard come out of myself—"Take it away! *Kill it!*"

Yes, *kill it.* I was not thinking of him, not of the baby, of course. But of that force which was depriving me of the power to think, to decide, to *be.* It is no longer *being* when one is no more than a pain, an animal ripped open and shrieking, inhabited by an incomprehensible yet perfectly everyday disaster. An admired disaster, like all the rest. Does one not say 'a fine storm', 'a splendid earthquake', 'a beautiful cancer'? Delighting in the event, the good old midwife observed, "Oh, it was a lovely delivery. You could hear her shrieking the other end of the street!"

Whence this horror? But also whence that peace that comes before it? The reciprocal movement that one continually finds, the swing of the pendulum that one's eyes insist upon following. "So long as I am pregnant," says the young mother. "So long," says the invalid to himself, "as I am given up . . ." Yes, so long as they have, as I have, an alibi, they really cannot be required to think, to live *as well*. As soon as they are ill, as soon as they are fulfilling a woman's 'sacred functions', or have four children, or are poor, or old, or (why not?) are 'artists' . . .

There is no counting all the possible alibis. People have such a very great deal of imagination! You have only to hear them announcing "I have four children" as they push into the cinema in front of you, or "I fought at Verdun" because they have buckled the left wing of your car . . . But I see that my alibis are deceitfully coming back to their familiar ground. I was talking about death. The peace of the death alibi or what stands for it. Peace, renunciation, which resembles consent as closely as falsehood does truth—the merest hair's breadth apart. But once death, illness, the four children (and art) are *accepted* they can no longer be used for alibis, refuges : from then on you have to try to live.

As far as I am concerned, it is not death that distresses me, but dying without having reached acquiescence, without having reached the point at which one can make one's body bow to its own destruction (and yet without renunciation). It is not writing that distresses me, but writing without yet controlling that nature to which the work should bow, without renunciation. What distresses me in love is the effort that has to be made in turning it to the direction that I think it ought to take, yet at the same time leaving it all its natural spontaneity. In poetry it is the double game of reality's two faces. And in life it is that death which one must accept and yet not serve. I would rather say, indeed, which one must make subservient to oneself. Make use of it to live, not to sleep.

Consent without renunciation, may not that perhaps be a guiding principle?

concierges

It seems to me that the extreme attraction of the 'passions', the worship of them (which I fear to such a degree because I am only too much under their sway) can arise only from a dismal impotence, from at least a mental impotence. Can one revere the passions when one knows them? Alibis still: it is not my fault. I am not to blame. The fascination of the passions, the fascination of death: a double face. You dread them; you long for them. How the worthy people love to talk about these childbed shrieks (which I beg pardon for having displayed at this point; but it was only as a case in point) and these writhings in agony! To talk about them: not to take them into real consideration. For who lives his life agreeing that it should be limited and realizing that it is limited? Almost nobody. Yet on the other hand almost everyone likes talking about death, sniffing at death, and excusing himself for not knowing how to live by the fact of death.

It is only sufferings that go beyond the human scale, prodigious atrocities and rivers of blood, that really delight both sick-room women and journalists. Concierges, old women of every kind who are to be seen in the evening, dozing on straw-seated chairs in front of hideous, artless lodges, layers-out, readers of police-court news, washers of the new-born, I have said it before and I say it again, you are Fate in its modern shape.

Just think of what she means to a whole building, that lowly overbearing woman who dwells in the murky lair where she spins her fatal thread in a dense atmosphere of carpet slippers and simmering beans! Concierges. Loved or loathed, you find them again after wars, partings or funerals, unchanging figures in striped overalls, ready, in the smelly darkness, to offer you the 'nice cup of coffee' that helps you survive, or to utter the word that sets the brand of infamy upon your conduct in these vicissitudes.

It is only in these dwellings and in a few particularly slummy rooms in which mounds of rags gently rot in their burst containers, that there flourishes, in its uncontaminated state, that cult of the fatal event, that liking for death which only occasionally we find on our own lips. Dispensing with the base mediation of intelligence, curses or praises flow in one direction or another with the violence of the absurd and the pitiless strength of great natural cataclysms.

If the Boss is the symbol of the Void that chooses to be the Void, for her part the Concierge is a tolerable allegory of Nature. At times she is a foster-mother and she lavishes undeserved attentions upon you. ("And suppose I make you a little dish of sweetbreads for this evening? Yes, yes, you are looking right pale. I'll make you eat it all up, you see if I don't"—and she is downright unbiddable.) And at others, with no greater apparent cause, she is unnaturally harsh, and makes you live in a perpetual winter, cutting off post, plumber and fuel. ("What now? I really can't be running up with telegrams every five minutes.")

Concierges! You love death; death is your friend. It gives you a chance to be useful ("I know how to wash a corpse," they say proudly), and to turn an honest penny ("I will look after everything"), but above all, above all, Fatality is your theme. You deck it out, coax it, expand it; and it is your anecdotes, full of sense, full of pith, that best translate that complex feeling that draws us with a most alluring giddiness towards the edge of the gulf.

the concierge's monologue

"You can never tell who is going to die and who is going to live," says the concierge. "It's always the best that leave us. Take the gentleman on the first floor, for example—a gentle man, such a gentle man; and he had everything you could want to be happy—car, telly, fridge and a good home; the lady looked after him beautiful. Well, there you are: he goes and catches a cold, him, a gentleman that looked after himself, and fairly reeked of eucalyptus—he did indeed—and always wore a muffler when he came back from the office and a little something from the chemist—he was never mean over that, though on Boxing Day you might whistle for it. What I mean to say, a person as looked after himself as well as he could. And then phut, in one week— [a gesture of cutting down]. But when the mark is on you, what can you do about it?"

A commiserating nod of the head. Then a fatalistic movement of the arms: no man can escape his fate. Then a few details, given with a portentous, scientific air.

"They opened the body, just fancy. Who can tell if they did not suspect the lady, or the daughter? There was something fishy about the will, I should say. Well, inside he was all black— black as ink, they say. And in the tubes, it seems, there was *knots*! Because he worrited so, you see, he was all *knotted* inside. And in the end, it wasn't the coughing that killed him, but another disease. I told you he was a marked man."

She sips her coffee: a drop falls in her green wool front and with total unconcern she rubs it with her finger.

"What's bad for some is good for others," says the concierge. "Now the young lady on the first floor will be able to have a high old time with her gentleman-friend. You should see how fond of one another they are! I have seen them on that bench there, kissing for twenty minutes on end. And what a rage he did get into, the father! He caught sight of them from a good way off one day, and the young man made himself scarce, but he went for the girl with his umbrella, and I give you my dying oath it was no laughing matter. Such a gentle man! She wasn't able to move out of the house for three days."

She sighs and gets up heavily (yet she looks young: perhaps forty. A fat, soft, fair woman who may turn into something horrible) and goes to replace the coffee-pot on the gas, that sacred flame that is never put out.

"I helped them, I did, those turtle-doves. He would give me a letter or a message. He was all smiles to me, but I was not taken in. Perhaps it was him as advised the daughter to . . . eh? Who'll ever know? That's what love is."

And so these inexhaustible lips pour forth, all as part of the same flow, their flood of monstrous suppositions, ghastly descriptions, philosophic adages and revolting sentiment. And at the bottom of it all, death; and at the bottom of it all, the absurd. This dead man such a gentle man (because he is dead)—who beats his unfortunate daughter (unfortunate at this moment, but perhaps a poisoner the next, who can tell? May be she too is *marked*?), and the lovers on the bench, the sweet pair of lovers (because lovers), but who, as soon as they leave their role, the twenty-minute kiss, and their prop, the time-honoured bench, become "capable of anything". These are the *characters* of the tale the concierge builds up; and it will be observed that each of the actors plays several roles as he comes into contact with one or another of the great changeless figures, Death, Love, Money, Jealousy, which endow him with life like a marionette and which justify him entirely in the eyes of our pythoness.

The concierge, faced with these changes of aspect, cries, "That's life!", and this exclamation reappears at every conjuncture at which it seems to her that an overpowering current sweeps a man and his poor little personality asunder, deprives him of his feeble will, and compels him to some astonishing outburst or some sudden transformation. Thus the thing that most often makes her cry "That's life!" is death: I have often remarked the fact, and it makes me think.

For after all I love 'life', in the concierge's meaning of the word. I love loving, writing, having babies. I love a fine show in the street, the open-air dancing on July 14. I love being angry and being carried away with joy. I love eating and drinking too much. I love swimming, and walking in the wind. I love laughing, making scenes and crying at the cinema. Beyond all I love festivals, the carefully planned long-drawn-out meals, the candles in the coloured wooden chandelier, too much fruit on an enormous dish, too much wine in the earthenware jugs, too many people, too much smoke, the prodigious tart, the children's over-excitement, a hasty box on the ear, the steaming pancakes, the gleaming balls on the Christmas tree, and I should like to cut myself in slices like the rye-bread on the wooden table and hand myself out to everybody there. I love my relations because they are my relations, my children because they are my children. I love my husband and myself and my work, my friends, the world and mankind. And basically I adore making love and having babies, shrieking as I do so. Tradition, do you see. "My reactionary side," as the left-wing young woman who has abortions as part of her role so kindly tells me.

This splendid picture of family feasts and ties of blood, also includes funerals. Death. Shrieks. The "I can't begin to tell you how he suffered" that slyly brings in the "things being what they are, there will always be some who . . . and others who . . ." And straight away we reach the injustice that is better than a want of order, the fine feelings that do not make good literature, each man to his own trade, the cows, the politics that have nothing to do with sentiment and the benign indulgence for the inspired artist. How can one struggle out of it all? Yet I had a splendid future as a reactionary! Or as a concierge?

But it went quite wrong; let us say no more about it. So I love 'life'. Should I say I did love it? And I loved, and I do love, the idea of death, which sets a proper term to this adventure, which it would not be right to carry on indefinitely. What I do not like is that tendency (my own as well as other peoples') to drown oneself in this life, to lose oneself in it, to turn it into a premature death, even if it is only a 'little death'.

Unless, of course, it is done innocently. But is one ever entirely innocent? Is one ever entirely 'stupid' for want of being an angel? "I don't want to know it," say those great allegorical figures, the

Boss and the Corporal. So they do suspect that *it* has an existence?

I do not know what this *it* contains. But I do know that the suspicion leads to that inquiry which never leaves off once it has begun and which follows me even to the most commonplace

dinner with friends

I wonder why it is that one always comes back to love-stories. To what look like love-stories. Because fundamentally there is nothing falser than the stories of Etienne's loves—he is a fair-haired nordic painter, and he and his wife have asked me to dinner. No, do not be uneasy: we shall not speak about life and death, nor about falsehood, nor about politics. Let us talk like a woman's magazine, about a marriage that is not going right (Etienne and Renée), a perfect pair of lovers (Pierre and Suzanne), a stylish young woman (Clo), and a man (Jean) who loves virtue. A thoroughly commonplace dinner.

It takes place in a cramped flat, a flat not without a certain charm, in a pleasant old house. Every day the filthy staircase gives Etienne a confirmation of his artistic gifts. He also has a studio on the sixth floor made from three servants' rooms. Renée is not pretty—thin and swarthy; yet her face is quite delicate, with an old-ivory complexion and fine eyes (but after all *why* is she not pretty? The woman's magazine once more : you are pretty if you want to be pretty. Yes, ugly women too are pretty, etc. The woman's magazine knows everything.)

I suppose that for her part Clo is pretty : her spotted trousers and her plaited straw sweater and her elaborate hair-do assert that she is; and the fact that she does not eat enough, and that at odd intervals, gives her an agreeably langorous, weary look that softens her rather hard face.

Renée dresses in an utterly inconspicuous manner (English tailor-mades and cashmire jerseys), arranges the table with great care (variegated napkins, very organized dishes of fruit, a twisted vine-branch on the mantelpiece standing out very well against the whitewashed wall), the perfect hostess, the woman offered up on the altar.

Etienne will wear his filthy old white pullover and his paint-spotted trousers, and with a passionate shamelessness she will say, "Isn't he beautiful?" And indeed he is—chin rather weak, eyes rather wavering, but a fine upstanding figure with regular features and Scandinavian blue eyes and fair hair.

Then Pierre and Suzanne arrive, bearing fruit or flowers or some propitiatory offering such as wine or cheese, by way of begging pardon in advance for hearing only one another, seeing only one another, existing only for and through one another.

As usual Jean will come well after everybody else. He comes in breathless and anxious, with a worried expression: he always has some fresh misfortune to talk about. A child with measles (he is the only one who has any children, and this gives him the right to extra furrows on his brow), the taxes, his wife Jeannette who undergoes every disease known to man. He is allowed to have his say.

At last Renée dishes up: it is past nine. Etienne leaves the table to put on a record. ("Louder!" says Clo. "Not so loud," begs Jean-who-has-had-a-dreadful-day: all his days are dreadful.) Everything is ready, Renée's 'speciality' (*moules marinières* or couscous or something of that sort, I forget what) is steaming on the table, everyone grasps his napkin and the meal begins.

Pierre and Suzanne relish the mussels (or the couscous). "Those mussels weren't bad at all, were they? And Renée was . . .Didn't you think Clo's spotted trousers . . .?"

They have never left the cosy little room that they have made for themselves. They gaze out of its window: they talk privately to one another. They are at a play, unseen in a warm, dark box; they feel amusement and indignation, but they are cut off from the others by a row of footlights or by a wall—they are *under cover*. This is a state of affairs that everybody finds convenient.

They bother nobody and they are easily classified—a pair of lovers. And it is so comforting, that non-aggression pact that they have signed with the world in general! They are asked out a great deal: "They are delightful!" Suzanne works for a publisher, Pierre at the Musée de l'Homme—he is an ethnologist, but a chair-borne ethnologist who classifies other people's travels, collects anecdotes; he is a rather disillusioned, charming man, small, quick, with a lively black eye; and she too is slim and lithe —you would think they were related. And their way of standing quite next to one another, tight, like birds, makes people smile. Besides, they have a perfectly lovely flat and a great many contacts. Is theirs a love-story?

Renée spares no pains: she prides herself upon having everything perfect although they are poor. As for the mussels (we will suppose it was mussels), she got up at six to get them at the market; and as for the pretty stemmed glasses, she has collected them one by one at auctions in the Charente, where she spends her penurious holidays with an aunt. "I really have to console myself for Etienne not being there," she says, in a certain tone. Everybody knows that Etienne makes no claim to holidays.

"You know that I can't cope with these holidays that you take at the same time as everybody else. I find organized leisure utterly destroying . . ." says Etienne, also in a certain tone. He prefers to spend August in Paris, where you find him rather drunk early in the morning with his arm round an ugly creature (a hundred times uglier than Renée) he has picked up at the Grande Chaumière or outside some tenth-rate studio and to whom he declares his passion with an ardour that is as sincere and short-lived as a flash of lightning. Some ungainly American, an Irish girl who drinks with him, a dazzling Italian whom he takes about everywhere and abandons on the twelfth day, no one knows why, in favour of a dirty-haired Scandinavian without the smallest apparent charm whom he has picked up in the underground and whom he says he wants to marry.

He even writes this to Renée and with a ravaged face she shows the letter to a dozen people, asserting that she will not stand in the way of his happiness; and she goes back on September 1 loaded with little ornaments, quite sure (and rightly so) that she will find everything in order.

"He is always mad about somebody," they say of Etienne, and of Renée, "She is quite marvellous. What is more, she suffers dreadfully." At least Pierre and Suzanne say it. Etienne says it: "It comes over me like a madness; I don't know why I absolutely cannot resist . . ." He is much given to holding his head between his hands, and he drinks from principle. His red picture is at a standstill; he has no regular contract; he is not really quite sure whether he is non-figurative or non-concrete or even perhaps (why not?) primitive. He swallows passion after passion, as if they were aspirins.

This evening he discovers Clo, who has been their friend for ages. He eats fewer and fewer mussels, drinks more and more white wine (it is delightfully chilled, in spite of the lack of refrigerator, oh perfect Renée) and sets himself to falling in love with Clo, flinging all idea of the red picture, the absence of contract, the bank-account only just keeping its head above water thanks to Renée's noble efforts, far into the shadows of his unconsciousness (as one hastily stuffs dirty clothes into a cupboard).

His attitude grows more tender, he listens to nobody but Clo, looks at her alone; everything vanishes, and each glance, each glass of wine is a revelation that thrusts his unwelcome awareness farther back.

Pierre-and-Suzanne exchange a look that is both saddened and (how can one put it?) comfortable. What a disaster this fickleness of Etienne's is! Poor Renée, who is growing extremely restless, upsets a glass, utters jokes that misfire. ("So you only have eyes for Clo this evening?") They have never deceived one another; almost never quarrelled. Suzanne has such an admiration for Pierre's work! She laughs so heartily at his stories! She understands his vulnerable side so well—he is very sad because he is not creative. And she knows how to soothe him and convince him of the importance of what he writes; whereas in his turn he pets her, lets her play her little-girl part at the age of thirty-two, teases her about her liking for detective-stories, fairs and vanilla ice-cream.

What an additional comfort the sight of this disunited couple is for them! Besides, they are genuinely sorry for the unfortunate Renée, who now tells Suzanne, who has come to help her in the kitchen, and Jean, who is ready to take up the burden of other people's cares as well as his own (he has a certain preference for the former, indeed), "I never can keep a friend who is a woman. He falls in love with them *all*, every time. I shall have to get used to it."

During dessert Suzanne and Pierre, moved by pity, hold hands under the table. Jean, with the agreeable consciousness of performing a good action ("Not only do I spend eight hours at the office, put up with Jeanette and her illnesses, see to the children when I come home and even sometimes get the meals ready, but what is more I bring comfort with me wherever I go . . ."), savours his real tiredness like an uncommon sensation and converses on dreary topics with Renée (she thanks him with a look : "It is no good at all, but I am touched").

Etienne is three parts drunk, and he puts his arm round Clo's barely-resisting shoulders, stubbornly saying to himself, "This is the woman I should have had! This one! And I shall have her. I must!" And Clo, "I am loved! He loves me! It is happening to me—I am loved, he thinks I am beautiful, he will live with me, a man of my own, absolutely my own. Renée is nothing to him, etc."

Clo is twenty-eight; but she is so slim, so willowy, her hair is so well done, her way of dressing, her tastes and her behaviour so dashing that no one would guess that she was an ugly child, the daughter of a little hairdresser in Angoulême by a Jewess, who was very good-looking, but who had to remain in hiding throughout the war: a double misfortune. Clo told herself, "I shall never be loved," and she does not really quite believe in Clo, with her varnished bead necklaces, her spotted trousers, her youthful carriage and her phoney beauty which is so much in fashion : or rather she does believe in it all, this evening and through Etienne's eyes. She wants to believe in it.

The room is suddenly lit up with a quite particular light, words clash into one another; under the power of eyes and of wine, faces change their appearance. Renée is suffering in a really spectacular manner and it makes her look almost beautiful : suffering is what she can do best. Pierre and Suzanne gaze at the sight, fondling one another in the darkness; in their happiness they must indeed feel superior to Etienne and Renée. And Jean forgets that he promised to do the washing-up when he got home; he helps Renée to suffer, and he feels himself radiating goodness, dripping with it (a feeling that he does not get from the washing-up).

In a word, it is a thoroughly successful dinner in which everyone has done his job and fulfilled his role—spectator, lover, artist, drunkard, victim, apostle . . . But where did they go to dine—Jean, Pierre, Suzanne, Renée, Etienne and Clo *themselves*, if there is a Pierre, Suzanne, Clo, who is not solely this performer of an already-written part, this acquiescent prisoner of a convention that excuses him from taking any initiative; for after all what are they doing here, uttering the words that are expected of them, throwing one another the ball with such care (what if she were to break the Charente glasses!) each inscrutable to the rest, enclosed in comfort, bitterness, pride, sensuality or suffering? Is it really worth while all coming together in order *thus to bear witness to each other's identity*?

And to a sham identity into the bargain. The celebration of a rite, like going to a gallery (La Gioconda, No. 3,663), or talking business (How much did you say, now?) the celebration of a rite in which one is an accomplice, in the same way as the prostitute who puts on harness or dresses herself as a bride. One puts on an appearance of charm or of suffering, one goes through the dance of love and of death; and where is the love in it at all? A rite, a dance-step, the easiest there is to learn. But what of it? It is all very commonplace.

So where does my distress come from? A thoroughly Parisian dinner, after all, at the same time quite ordinary and quite 'romantic', as the women's magazines understand the term, of course. The background—an old house 'done over': the characters with stylish professions—ethnologist, painter, mannequin (Clo), chemical engineer (Jean): the latent plots (Pierre and Suzanne who will or will not get married); Jean, who no longer loves his wife but who will find her again when his youngest child almost dies of measles; Clo, who loves Etienne but who will sacrifice herself; Renée, who loves Etienne and who will wait for him; Etienne, who . . . everything is there to make a splendid woman's novel. It is everyday life, the stupid, harmless problems that affect everybody—that is what one likes reading at night in bed, or in the bath as one is 'relaxing'; stories that have no connexion with art, the war in Algeria and the existence of God. Stories that have no meaning—stupid, dead tales.

Looking back, what I see is a dinner of dead people; a dinner in a novel, at which puppets utter dialogue that has already been written, filled with 'psychological' retorts and 'revealing' grimaces. Yes, I see Renée again, her looks enhanced by that blaze of suffering which changes her face and which she carefully keeps alight; and once more I hear the words that are *exchanged*—and how exact it is, that term.

"I really have to console myself for Etienne's not being there."

"You know that I don't like these fixed-date holidays . . . Paris is very pleasant in August."

"And the women of Paris. Or rather of America."

"Why not?" says Etienne. "I am very fond of those from Angoulême, too."

Clo puts in a little shrill laugh.

"Everyone knows your universal kindness," says Renée. "But it is with the Scandinavians that he has his greatest successes. Oh yes you do, and you are quite proud of it. He literally forces me to read the letters of all the women who admire him. It is perfectly extraordinary—they want to kill themselves for him. What is more, you really believe it, don't you? He genuinely believes that he is in love with you, Clo. Besides, he can only paint when he is drunk or in love: I put up with it . . ."

Renée's face is really extraordinary. She smiles, she grits her teeth; she is sparkling, brilliant, tense, sharp; it hurts her so much that she could cry out; it is killing her; she is happy.

Pierre-and-Suzanne : It was ghastly. Etienne is a sadist; oh sweetheart, sweetheart . . . (Sheltered, utterly sheltered from all that; all that, which revolts them and yet seen from afar, from their theatre box, attracts them just a little. But how happy they are to go home!)

Jean : As for all these torments, these temptations, I gaze down upon them from a great height; it is charming to contemplate their utter futility, my dear Renée, and if there is anything I can do . . . yes, yes, I shall ring you up tomorrow at eight . . . (Virtue is not very jolly, but then nor is vice either, thinks he.)

Clo : I am mad, I know he doesn't love me : one night, just one night, why not? I am free, and passionate; I have no prejudices, I am mad, it's gorgeous . . . (Did I put on my new Maidenform bra?)

Etienne : I must have her; I want her, now, tonight, right away. I am overflowing with strength and fire and virility, I am being carried away by a whirlwind, I *am* the whirlwind: quick, quick.

And of course Renée is prepared to go and shut herself up in the bathroom—what am I saying? She is ready to turn down the bed, to undress Clo, to . . .

But there they stop me, saying no, this is not a commonplace dinner : at all events that pair, those two are *monsters!*

It is easy to say. People absolutely love talking about monsters. Eichmann is a monster. The concierge-who-ill-treated-her-five-year-old-nephew is a monster. The FLN and the OAS are all monsters, of course. The man who goes to the brothel. The communist. Céline. That child is a monster : just imagine it, he failed his exam *on purpose*! The Nazis, the Fascists, the Germans, the Arabs, the Reds, the killers, the vivisectionists, the Others . . . all monsters. The standard monster is the sex-maniac who rapes a little girl of ten. "No, he did not rape her; he only loved her," says someone. "That's worse," says the Boss. "At least rape is *natural.*"

Crime is natural, too. But does Etienne's and Renée's 'crime' (by which I mean the false note they give out and the disagreeable sensation that I feel in their company) consist solely in not being natural? Let us forget Clo. Clo vanishes. In my opinion it would look very well if she were to go off to Nepal with a producer far out on the left wing. She would come back a vegetarian. So exit Clo.

Who complains about this adventure? Not Clo, who goes on playing the part of the free, emancipated modern woman (but because of her new set of friends her love for winsome capriciousness changes into a more manly, candid and straightforward freedom, and she wears an officer's macintosh).

Not Etienne, who has not had to put up with a refusal at the Salon de Mai, since he did not submit a picture : he is a half-wit, not a failure; and there is a great difference between the two.

And not Renée, who had "always told you so." She exults. After all, since "she had always told you" that Clo would be Etienne's mistress and that Etienne would get tired of her, she can almost tell herself that without her nothing would have happened. It is possible for her not to feel the humiliation of a betrayed wife, but rather the pride of one who has chosen to suffer.

This choice worries me rather. Why this choice? What was it meant to hide? (Children pretending to limp to distract the attention of passers-by whom they fear—an everyday occurrence.) Is it a reaction of the same kind on Renée's part? A complex? Let us go into it. It is obvious that she goes on about Etienne's success with women far too much : she talks about it, she emphasizes it, and it almost looks as though she were urging him in that direction. From all this she has herself caught something rather queer, rather ambiguous : she will go to the point of crying up Etienne like something she has to sell, to the point of entertaining his mistresses and encouraging them, if not actually seducing them. Indeed, one will slowly come to wonder whether Etienne is going along this road in front of her, or whether he is merely following behind. He is no longer sure himself. However that may be, he is closely bound to her. Perhaps that is what she wants. But does not this crop of women she offers him and the pride she takes in her deus ex machina role hide the more private wound of not having been able to cure him of his doubts and his confusion?

One might also make a case for revenge : suppose Renée knew that by urging Etienne (incapable of loving her) to follow this dissipated course she was preventing him from solving his problems as a creative artist? In fact you can make a case for anything you like, on the basis of this little item in the Advice to the Lovelorn column—a man who deceives his wife and a woman who suffers.

It does not matter what. And to anything carefully studied, thought about, true, even to a slight degree, that you may put forward, people will cry out *What monsters!* Or else, *Why pick out such disagreeable characters?* Now what is disagreeable is neither Renée nor Etienne (nor Clo, nor Jean, nor me)—what is disagreeable to the reader is that the matter is looked into rather deeply. For after all on the surface Jean is a good sort, Clo a delightful scatterbrain, Etienne an impassioned, inconstant 'artist', Renée an unhappy woman who is full of deserving qualities and who is not pretty. What is monstrous is saying that the problem does not lie there. Not *only* there. Renée is proud and complicated, Clo is afraid of the world, Etienne is afraid both of failing and of succeeding. A dark forest of symbols into which one does not choose to wander. The hollow outward appearance is preferable —the 'character', as light as a fritter and easily digestible.

Or else, because 'this is real life', there is too great a desire to get lost in the devious intricacies of the determining causes. Peering at Renée, Etienne and Clo as though they were mishapen insects whose carapace has taken on its shape unaided—a carapace whose hopeless prisoners they are—like the concierge, one cries "They are *marked*!"

So is there no possible agreement between the derisory freedom of the novelette and the Wagnerian fatalism of my slippered prophetess, no possible relationship? And if Renée cannot be explained either by her will or by her nature (and not only her but myself, this book), how then *can* Renée be explained and expressed?

The fact that things cannot be explained in their entirety, is one of those obstacles I am continually coming up against with the discouraging regularity of the tide. I had to set about reflecting in order to find out that the act of reflection was not in itself enough to grasp the nature of things. Here again there was the double face, the double movement, the swinging that I could not manage to resolve and which perhaps it was not desirable to resolve. This motion was life itself, and to freeze it would have been to kill it.

But in that case what about my inquiry? Was it not entirely invalidated? Did I not emerge from the absurd only to fall into the arbitrary? Both before and after I still lacked a dimension. My true research ought to be not the substitution of one of the faces of my truth for another, but the discovery of what binds them together, their relationship. Unless I did this I should find nothing but my own loneliness again at the end of my thought, like a person who goes round and round in the middle of a forest: these faces, places, moments, would be nothing other than the clues to a puzzle, all of which would come to the same answer— my own name.

I was especially haunted by this thought after the dinner at Renée's; and the cause of this was its trappings. Her perfect taste was always mentioned, and that very evening Jean had congratulated her upon those glasses from the Charante, completely simple peasant glasses, cylindrical and standing on a foot, but so perfect in their proportions that we had all admired them.

"This proportion has a visible existence for each one of us," I said to myself, "And it proves that between us there exists a unity of beauty, a common denominator. By admiring a proportion together we demonstrate the existence of a value outside ourselves, an objective value."

This agreement between us, however fleeting it may have been, made me happy for quite a while. I loved Renée for having spent a whole afternoon in successfully arranging a bunch of flowers, a basket of fruit, in finding the right place for some object, a white vase against an ochre wall. What, fundamentally, comes closer to what I was doing—to what I am doing, as I gather a thousand little fragments, searching for the moment at which the mosaic shall be complete and perfect, with each of its component parts both independent and inseparable from the others, bound to them by this famous connexion?

But if the relationship between the ochre and the white means no more than 'Renée', and if the relationship between ink and paper only means 'me', can the two of us, absurd objects, assign ourselves a place in an absurd world, *unconnected* with anything whatsoever? If it is enough to mean something, to mean oneself, in what way is reflection either good or useful? Does not the Boss assert, with his slightest word, his lightest gesture, a monolithic stupidity vast enough to inspire Dubuffet?

No, I could not accept that. To accept being no more than

oneself is the same as agreeing not to exist. But refusing to be one-self is the source of many and many an error.

And here I must tell a moral tale. The story of Jean, who loved virtue too much. It should have a triple value: that of acting as an example for me, that of letting me draw breath for a moment (and the reader too, who is being worn out by my laborious meditation), and lastly, perhaps, that of clearing me from the heavy suspicion of virtuousness that the evilly-inclined cause to hang about me. Indeed, I wonder whether the last may not perhaps be the most important. And since my parentheses and asides proliferate, why not take advantage of it to bawl out in exasperation, as I often long to do, that

I am not virtuous at all!

Or if I am, it is without meaning to be. After all, since people assure me that it is so, there may be something in what they say. The strange thing is that the assertion always come from people who want to be unpleasant to me. I never hear any such thing from my friends, who are on the other hand quite unanimous in pointing out to me my disagreeable personality, the sudden urgent need of sleep that comes over me as early as eight in the evening, my lack of humour and my frivolity—the two combining, it seems, in a perfectly intolerable manner. But not one of them, at any time, ever blames me for excessive virtue, nor thinks himself obliged to write an article upon it. And yet there must be some-thing very irritating about this hypothetical 'virtue', for a respect-able woman of importance to take the trouble to reproach me with it in writing, on the first page of a newspaper!

But after all why shouldn't I be virtuous if I like? And how do my poor babies (whom this woman of importance, and others, always fling in my teeth: yet other people have had four children without causing any uproar!) come to be mixed up in it? In the first place how can they tell whether I had them on purpose? It might be just an unfortunate coincidence and the way one is made: is it my fault that I am not sterile? Come, this picking on mothers of families practically amounts to racialism! True enough, I do get up early. But then I have always got up early and gone to bed early too (like the great majority of people), without for that reason ever having astonished the general public! It may be said, What does your woman of importance matter? But if she irritates me and puzzles me, she does so in the same way as the *Paris-Match* photographers: she crystallizes an uneasiness of the same kind. The uneasiness of seeing a sequence of apparently inconsequential random instants turned into a motionless and tolerably ludicrous image.

There are no inconsequential instants: that is one good thing that this curious intrusion, this unmerited blame has already taught me. When you think you are feeling your way from boisterous adolescence to hesitating adolescence, from baby to baby, book to book, when you think you are going along rather aimlessly, suffering a little, forgetting a great deal, all of a sudden you find, when you are thinking or writing a book, that you have not forgotten anything at all; when you are trying to understand, are afraid of understanding, and when you do understand, all at once other problems, other books (and, incidentally other babies) appear. In short, *while one is living,* with a certain feeling of pottering, of putting together something rather lopsided (but well-intentioned for all that) made out of all the odds and ends that come to hand ("So I am an odd and end?" says Jacques, none too pleased), suddenly there comes this amazing revelation: one is a *virtuous* creature! However devoid of prejudices one may be one still cannot avoid starting: "Lord above, what have I done?"

Then one calms down. It would have been no worse, after all, if I had driven about in a Jaguar, quaffing whiskey (I do drink it sometimes, and very willingly): there again the image would have been fixed, firmly bogged down in a picture on page three, with the fastest car caricaturing speed and finally denying it.

Thus everything is distorted as soon as that which, for want of a better word, I have called *falsehood* makes its appearance—that which is not truth's opposite but its reflection, its mirror, its death. Mysterious phenomenon of transmutation, that leaves me wondering every time, and almost filled with admiration. It is not so much the words that lie as the manner in which they are said; and the word *false* is never more exactly used than in the expression *to sing false*. But can you go and stop others singing false for you? On a theme that you have provided them with? That is not the important thing : the important thing is to know how not to hear and to succeed in humming one's own personal little melody as much in tune as possible. And it is that which brings me to Jean's story, which I shall not tell after all. In its way, this tale is over-virtuous too, although it is not virtuous at all. It is too obvious and too studied; it is too clear that it means something. It is a demonstration, not a story; and Jean himself is too boring for his story not to be boring too.

He has botched his life, just as one botches a book when one wants to prove something too much. It is dull and flat : one is not quite sure where the mistake lies, but it is there all right . . . His life makes me think of the report of a publisher's reader : *The characters are psychologically true, the plot is well constructed, the writing is correct and clear; but nothing excites the reader, nothing comes alive. Why publish this manuscript rather than another?* Yes, why?

Jean is married out of virtue, a father out of virtue, and out of virtue an active member of some political party or other; yet he never manages to give a positive image of virtue. It is in vain that he has chosen a dreary wife, that he does the washing-up, goes with a busy air to group meetings (during the holidays he has put himself down for lecture courses and every week-end he has to go down to some resort in Normandy or Brittany to join his wife and the twins) : for all that one still has the feeling that he completely invents these obligations.

They are not the reverse of the medal and he is not a happy father in whose life the measles are merely a chance occurrence—no, the measles are his reason for existence, much more than the twins, who are but the occasion for the measles, the dismal performers. Furthermore, when they have not got the measles, Jeannette, like a good wife, hurries forward with a broken leg, or else the factory cuts down its staff; at the time of Salan's putsch Jean himself caught bronchitis and he hurried about the town (Jean, not Salan) in his little Renault with a temperature of 104 (102 would be shabby) handing out tracts or *converging upon the airfields*. Not that I blame those who did converge or who were prepared to converge, on foot or . . . etc. I was one of them myself.

But the temperature of 104 is altogether too much. It is the over-emphatic adjective, the actor's miscalculated gesticulation, Freud's revealing slip of the tongue: Jean overdoes it. Let us abandon him. We will leave him to himself. I don't feel strong enough to plunge into this life of his that has become abstract through being so studied, so deliberate. Just one more word. Going to see the Marais with an organized lecture-tour, Jean was in one of the old houses, and by mistake he went into a bathroom (antique?) in which a girl was having a bath. He clapped the door to. This single stroke describes him. Let us too close the door. What I wanted to say about Jean's virtue is this: after all, so long as it is a question of brothels, a disguise is a disguise. A whore dressed up as a bride and a whore dressed up as a horse amount to much the same: they are both disguises. (And a whore can be *disguised* as a whore, and indeed most thoroughly disguised.)

It seems to me that there is as much similarity between Jean and Etienne as there is between a grasping father and a spendthrift son—the chief preoccupation of both is money. Both, the prodigal and the miser, disguise themselves, and they pay the penalty—they are bores. Jean is a bore because of his colourlessness, his 'good employee' side; Etienne because of his banality, the lawless, unbridled 'artist'. Their disguise lacks style. They be-

come interesting once more if their bodies can be seen through
their disguise (whereupon the cry of *Monsters* rings out): in the
case of Etienne the liking for and the fear of failure, and in the
case of Jean that equivocal pity for suffering. The two planes, the
play of light and shade: a fortunate combination may give rise
to a spark of poetry. That is vice's whole attraction, and the
attraction of disguises.

But how much more readily will this attraction spring from the
quest for truth, with its uncertainties and its perpetual changes of
register, than from chance, for then it can only break through
some rip in the disguise, the falsehood. I believe that poetry cannot do without truth: that is its particular virtue.

But if this is granted, what is the good of writing anything
other than a novel? Is it not in the novel alone that the double
plane of truth—the truth of my characters and their struggle for
and against it; my own personal truth and my struggle for and
against it; and that relationship between them and me, that relationship between their truth and mine—can be brought into
being, embodied without distress? What is the point in trying to
analyse, to explain what *is,* what *lives,* so much more fully, in a
piece of work or in a life?

So I shall write a novel. What about? About anything at all.
Because of the confidence that I formerly had, on an equal footing
with nature and now on an equal footing with myself, I hope that
whatever I may write, it will all mean something. That whatever
I may do, it will all mean something. These are words that have
impressed me ever since I first heard them : Whenever you eat or
drink, do it for the love of the Lord.

For myself I interpret this as, Whatever you do, do it truthfully.
Because the thing that disturbed me, arousing that strange distress
within that I have spoken about (and which I might very well
call *the semantic distress*) was not so much that books and people
were *bad* as that they were not *truthfully* so. It was not so much
the ugliness of a personality that disturbed me, but rather its dis-

guise—not so much concupiscence, violence and evil, as false concupiscence, compensating violence, false evil—but was there a genuine evil? Was not all evil above all an error? A void?

The producer's ritual, René's adultery, Jean's virtue, Marcel's love of art, Etienne's affairs and Renée's sufferings—the bond that linked them all was there. They were disguises. And the concierge's "that's life." Life disguised as life: the worst of all. No doubt without these masks their faces would have been none the more lovely; but at least they would have been their own. Visages that they could then have faced up to and, perhaps, have changed.

Perhaps. Of course everything depends on that perhaps. Hope and despair, what is called faith and what I still call courage. But the courage already lies in that look one directs at oneself without flinching from anything that it discovers—without the obstinate stupidity of the Boss: "I do not *want* to know it." Courage lies in the wanting to know, which solves nothing, but which has within itself all solutions. As Luc says, thinking is already taking sides. So is writing this book. And the others.

To live with truth. To want to do so. And to be able to do so. For some people freedom is so restricted! Revel, a sincere man and a man of good will, nevertheless makes game of Danilo Dolci, who asks the poverty-stricken Sicilians, "How do you live God?" That is to say: "What margin of freedom have you kept? Where for you is the choice between being truthfully and not being at all?" Some see this as a ridiculous question and one that is insulting when it is asked of men who are dying of hunger. Yet it is the only one that has any meaning, since it is the only one that can unfailingly uphold the duty of giving bread to men whom hunger prevents from being free. Bread sets free; but does not necessarily set free for good ends—that dear illusion of so many generous hearts. It sets a man free to choose: it often sets free for the bad, but man has a right to that choice and to that evil, without which he is no longer a man. Perhaps it was that which made the young

soldiers of S. laugh at the old women brought down to the level
of animals?

S. again

Deprived of freedom, of choice—they had either to fight or to
die of hunger, and all-powerful instinct forbade them to choose
death—but it might also have been said (and perhaps it was that
which prompted the laughter) that they were set free from choice,
set free from freedom. With no inner conflict, they fought without restraint, *innocently*. Animals. One says brought down to the
level of animals; but this 'degradation' implies that a flicker of
awareness remains. These lean beasts had none left, if indeed they
had ever had any at all.

There were two of them more nimble than the others who
quickly fastened upon bones and bread and hurried off to hide
themselves in the nearby alleys. Three went on fighting, almost
silently, with a low, dog-like growling from time to time. And the
young soldiers behind the barrack railings were three also: a big
young fellow who must have been in charge of the canteen and
who had thrown these scraps of food on the ground; then quite a
good-looking dark youth with a scornful expression; and the third
had a round head—an artless, sullen young man.

Two of the three women were extremely thin, and they were
dressed in ochre and black—great cloth sacks that flapped round
their angular bodies. One was almost entirely bald and her right
eye had a white film over it; but she had a splendid set of teeth,
and in her hunger-drawn face they looked like those of a corpse.
The other had long grey hair in thin plaits which were held back
by a kind of little turban or bandeau—a surprising remnant of
respectability. The third was almost corpulent, with a flaccid, un-
healthy fat: her red skirt, her torn flowered blouse, her one
slipper, were all indescribably filthy and malodorous. Presently the
struggle was reduced to a single combat between the first and the

third of the old women; the one with the white turban had received a damaging blow and had gone off groaning into a corner.

The dawn rose on the nearby barracks. It was no doubt going to be a fine day: the air was still cold but dry, and the sky with its remaining haze grew lighter minute by minute. There were trumpets in the distance, as there are in adventure-films, and white façades that would soon show splendid under the blue sky. I had got up early. What relationship was there between my well-being, the pure air, the solid shadows of the early dawn of fine days, and, behind that quickly-closed barred gate (as if they were protecting themselves from wild beasts), those three commonplace, amused, scornful, sullen faces; what relationship with that futile battle in the dust that seemed to be part of the morning, of nature, a mere convulsion of unknown animals . . .

The lean arms of the bald fighter weakened. For a moment her teeth sank into the shoulder of the fat one, who moaned, and the young fellow behind the bars (the biggest, the pleasant-looking one with curly hair) burst out laughing and cried "She is going to eat her!" But the fat woman made a cunning use of her weight. She rolled nimbly over on to the other, thus paralysing her for an instant, stunned her with a thrust of her head, a butt; and triumphing, sitting with all her weight on her opponent's body, she raised her broad, flat, toad-like head, looked at the curly youth doubling up with laughter the other side of the railings, and *laughed* too.

Set free from freedom, I was saying. Delivered from liberty. Yes, it was certainly a laugh of liberation, the laugh of an accomplice. To be sure she was laughing because she had won, but she was also laughing because she felt no kind of shame or humiliation in it. She laughed innocently. She had no choice: and may not the young soldier's laugh have arisen from that too? From seeing that there is a limit to human responsibility and that the metamorphosis of a man into an animal is one of the easiest to carry out successfully? Yes, there was certainly complicity in that laugh: no doubt it never crossed the mind of the well-fed young man with his look of a hairdresser's assistant from somewhere in the south, and a hint of a moustache on his sweating lip, that he himself might be brought to that pitch of starvation at which he should have to fight in the gutter for a bowl of meat; but to see that something as simple as starvation was enough to reduce that burden under which he laboured (like all of us) to nothing, made him laugh, and laugh with relief. "It's no more than that," his laugh seemed to say. "No more than that!"

Yes, it is no more than that, this freedom, this truth, which sorrow, illness, violent emotion, even a toothache may endanger at any minute. Or is it rather changed, diminished, yet still there? Varying with the infinite variety of human possibilities?

Luc says, "You will accomplish nothing by feeding your old women. Those charming little soldiers have stuffed themselves well, haven't they? It has not made them any better. Well then?" He goes on, pleased to be teaching me something, "Even the communists admit it: they are interested in the worker and not in the peasant—why? Because the worker is genuinely poor, so poor that more often than not he hasn't even any *being*. So long as he is utterly poverty-stricken he will demonstrate, get himself knocked about, stick up posters, lick envelopes—generous, unselfish, anything you like. No, I am not joking. Then as soon as he has got twopence he buys himself a car, he buys himself a television, and it's farewell to the comrades. He becomes bourgeois. But he is the same man. A better man, do you think?"

"Freer . . ."

"Free! But they don't give a damn about being free! They are scarcely 'freer' for a moment before they start chaining themselves up with things bought on credit, marriage, children, anything at all not to be unchained, free! A fine present to give them!"

"Yes, they do put chains on themselves; but chains are not put on them."

"Where is the difference?"

"In the choice."

My views really depress Luc. "To put it in a nutshell, you would like to raise people's standard of living so that they should be free to become swine like the rest?"

"Just so."

"How uncommonly moral," says Luc, shrugging.

I do not know whether it is moral or not. Maybe I am no more moral than I am virtuous. I do think that it is just. I believe that some people in this world have quite certainly too small a share in choosing: I observe that this share in choosing is often proportionate to the share of bread, the share of space. Let us give the bread: let us make room. Afterwards, if their choice is a mistake or an alibi, *it is nothing to do with us.* "Make room for potential swine?" says Luc. "You have got courage!" He said the word himself. Courage.

So here I am back from North Africa to my theme again, without any jolt. Courage. To my mathematical inclinations: proportion, relationship. To that bond which links me with my subject and my subject to the life of the world. I said that my subject was Cézanne at Aix. I could say that my subject is me in front of this book.

Presumptuous comparison? I can put it another way. For example, my theme is

Ghy in the workshop

I see her clearly enough, dark, with an olive complexion (that "green young girl" J.-P. Toulet speaks of), with a very slight lack of symmetry in her face which gives her her charm, and which she laments—an asymmetry from which she gets her sweet and hesitant look. A mild look, a hard voice—and the hardness coming a little too easily, a rather vulgar hardness. The challenge of her soft chin, raised in the air. A pretty girl: a winding-machine operator in a factory. Not tall, in spite of her prodigious high heels, but supple and shapely: violent, tense, shy, aggressive, very apt to burst into tears and foolish laughter. Parents separated: no drama, but unlimited meanness. Eleven years have passed, but the mother is still bitterly claiming two coal-buckets and a sewing kit that 'the other woman' kept.

Ghy lodges with her father, being put in a sort of box-room, a dark hole that is nevertheless continually passed through by other people: she lies flat on her stomach on her bed, eating unhealthy-looking goodies; and she lives glued to the glittering transistor. Oh, the twist! And Paul Anka! The father is a bloody nuisance, neither more nor less: he wants her wages and he wants her to make the evening spaghetti—a dish prepared by throwing the stuff hastily into boiling water with one of those meat-extract cubes in it.

The stepmother is a blonde; rather a dim-wit, says Ghy. She is house-proud and she loves her satin bedspread and her hire-purchase telly; and she is terribly, terribly fussy. "Your under-clothes everywhere—you behave as if you were in your own house!" Everybody goes out to work except the little brother, who is nine and who is doing well at school and who will be 'some-body'. Everyone comes home worn-out at seven and piles into the two rooms while the stepmother shouts, "Your feet, André! Pierrot, leave the milk alone! Oh, that girl!"

That girl is Ghy, who has turned the transistor up to full blast and, keeping time with her head, has forgotten the steak bought on the way home, which is now turning grey in the pan. Being fed up, that is Ghy's problem. How to get out of it? In the manner of Virginia Woolf she dreams of 'a room of one's own'. But what to put into it? The transistor, of course, and Paul Anka. And what then? Even thinking about it makes her feel fed up. As you may imagine, I am not going to go on for ever about these 'third-rate' characters in this 'sordid' dwelling, nor about these working-class subjects.

163

It may be that Ghy will fall in love with a worthy trade-unionist or with a teddy-boy and go to bed with the one although she loves the other, and weep because she cannot even weep in peace in her corridor-box-room. That is not important: what is important is that sinking down, that foundering in a quicksand, which means that Ghy, who is after all so lovable, so brown, so appealing with the divergent gaze of her green eyes ("Oh, I should love to be a nurse and sacrifice myself!" she says, just like a girl of the fashionable world: and then for a month she goes out sticking up posters with a handsome dark man who has the gift of the gab; then drops it), lives less and less, from one Saturday night's dance to the next (she does not dance with Arabs—would scorn it).

Then she is wild about Bouchaïeb for three weeks—it is disgusting what they do to them—fascist! Then, disgusted, she aborts herself with a probe, helped by her stepmother: and all these Arabs are the same, the dirty swine! From winding one coil to winding the next (it's tiring, working at the conveyor-belt, but at least there's no fuss; you do it without thinking about it; you do it without thinking about anything at all: make the same movement again and again and again . . .). Thought is drawn out at the rhythm of the conveyor-belt, drawn out thinner and thinner, vanishes like a piece of spaghetti, a thin ribbon of spaghetti dwindling fast to a thread . . .

Ghy is this thread. She winds her coils, she gets her pay; perhaps she goes and has a drink or maybe only a cup of coffee, and it is two hundred francs into the juke-box at one go. "Hell, I have forgotten the supper! Quick, noodles, an egg, an Oxo cube," and the transistor turned on full—but her dreams are indolent television dreams. It is of little importance that now she is 'going with' a married man: he has a room of his own, but it is in a place belonging to friends and you have to go through their living-room —Ghy is doomed to this lack of privacy.

The other affairs, the other transient rooms, the other people she 'goes with' hardly matter. In fact Ghy is not 'going with' anybody, not even with Ghy. The thought that is drawn out on the worn rubber belt cannot be distinguished any more. When they suggest that Ghy, who is a good operative, one who gives no trouble, should move on to another, better-paid, conveyor-belt, she refuses. "I like what I'm used to," she says. To work out her movements all over again, to work out even one of them, would be too much; it would be too much to be something else, even if it were only for a few days, than that machine which from now on works by itself, a well run-in, well oiled machine that runs on nothing : no, she does not want anything any more, she cannot cope with anything any more—farewell, splendid adolescent tempers, rages, posters, bicycle chains; goodbye. Empty, the conveyor-belt runs on.

"She has settled down," says her stepmother, "Paul will end up by getting a divorce." Yes, no doubt, Paul will end up by getting a divorce and everything will end happily on an ideal housing-estate in front of a bulging television, the bloated fruit of pains-taking coil-winding; and Paul will marry her and they will have family allowances, just as if they were in a novel by Mme Roche-fort.

That is not the question. But what is the question? It is not that which the parish priest asks, either : "You are not married?"

"What difference does that make?" says Ghy (at twenty she is insolent and she adds details: a little later, she is weary).

And in fact nothing is different except that empty conveyor-belt stretching away out of sight. "How do you live God?" Danilo Dolci would ask Ghy. But it would have come to the same thing if he were to ask her, "How do you live?" and even, "Are you still living?" People might object that the question is cynical, that Ghy is a victim of society (and perhaps even more so than the Sicilian peasants, for she is not hungry, and hunger sometimes awakens those who suffer from it). When the choice is between not living and living on coil-winding, luke-warm spaghetti, the tall grey chimneys of Puteaux, Paul and his slippers and the probe,

the end of the month and the beginning—so much alike, dear
God, so very much alike—why then the choice is no less than
heroic. If Ghy chose to live and to think, to live Ghy, to think herself Ghy, however restricted that thought might be, then Ghy
would have the courage of Cézanne. Married or not.

It is time that I should tell you that I know Ghy well and that
I like her, defeated by the weariness of living and being though
she is. For a moment she put up a struggle, unco-ordinated and
exaggerated, touching in its disproportioned efforts. Little sister.
Then dropped it. Victim. Do we manage so very much better?

We should have liked to help her: we could not. To have
guessed her truth, which would have helped her to live. Those
are discoveries that one can only make alone. Each person has
within him that truth which is as commonplace and as mysterious
as a figure—that freedom which is like a proportion. Proportion,
yes; or again relationship, golden number, ratio between these
natural forces, these restraints and these outbursts, and this self-
confrontation by the mind which is measuring up the material
that it has for building, gauging it, and which sets itself to work,
to its *own* work.

A hundred kinds of work; a hundred different truths. How do
you live God? What is the shape of your truth? There are some
that are quite astonishing, some very difficult to make out.
"Whenever you eat or drink, do it for the love of God." Do it in
truth. But if it is already hard to understand the form that truth
takes on for oneself, how much more dimly seen is the shape of
other people's truth? If it is psychologically difficult to ask a man
who is dying of hunger how he lives in reality, when merely living
is already a virtue for him, it seems almost more ridiculous to ask
it of others, whom the waves of life have worked into such strange
shapes, incrusting them with such strange growths, that they are
changed into irregular, shapeless objects whose apparent lack of
meaning, whose *picturesqueness*, takes on the surrealistic charm
of the absurd.

There is a strong temptation to index these curious forms that human activity (and human love) can assume—to describe them as if they were a strange submarine flora and fauna, entrancing to watch in the sea-green water no doubt, but separated from one for ever by another element. Nothing is easier than this zoologist's attitude: Ghy and Paul Anka, for example; the extraordinary radio programme that deals with popular music and in which a grave, pleasant voice analyses in the calmest way imaginable such pieces as *C'est ça l'amore*, and a tune from the *Cloches de Corne-ville*, speaking of 'orchestration' and 'resonant counterpoint'. And Frank Pourcell and his Magic Violins . . .

And the success of Cronin, whom Ghy devours with gasps of emotion, a genuine emotion, dreaming impossible dreams—a 'man in white' falls in love with her; oh, devotion, oh, leper colonies . . . One day, when she was seventeen, Ghy (who never passed her elementary examination), wrote a poem. I shall not reproduce it here, even in a transposed, transformed state. That would be desecrating a truly sacred moment—the moment at which Ghy, filled with wonder at the feeling of an embryonic thought moving within her, said gently, "I know it is not beauti-ful . . . But I can't believe that it was me who wrote that . . ."

Poem, ludicrous, distorted incrustation on the under-water rock, made up of haphazard deposits, mishapen enthusiasms, vital instincts—hideous and respectable object, poem that would delight the zoologist, the lover of the improbable picturesque, the unrivalled Woolworth tiara. And Ghy's notions of stylishness!

The Boss's life, his former sporting activities, his cups, which he polishes so lovingly. What did sport mean to him? A subject for inquiry. Of course, one may also talk about fashionable people, the duchess's salon; and that is amusing too, a salon under the water. It is no less diverting to move from one to the other, from the Boss's bar to the publisher's cocktail party: one has the feeling of visiting a silent aquarium—the dark, heated passage in the middle with its strange, reptilian warmth (the convolutions of the radiators incubating their green plants) and the illuminated glass of the tanks, the other plants in the water gently waving their fronds, those beings one gazes upon at one's leisure in the silence and warmth of one's isolation, the unperturbed calm of one's detachment, comparing the monstrous excrescences (even the agreeable becomes monstrous, so why not the monstrous agreeable?), the strange iridescent colours, the bubbles that these rare fish send up . . .

"Describe X's salon with the Monaco aquarium in mind. In oceanographic terms." One of Huxley's novelist heroes might take this as a subject for his novel. An aquarium with the glass four layers deep. It is not the author who is thinking and projecting himself by means of his novel, but his hero, who is himself separated from the theme by means of a second novel that he is supposed to be writing, and the theme is deliberately set farther off again by its oceanographic disguise. Can one isolate oneself more than this or take greater care of words, those dangerous explosives?

A novelist creates an imitation novelist with an imitation novel to write in which perhaps a novelist . . . It is quite a well-known technique in advertizing—you see it all over aperitif bottles. But these precautions, all these sheets of plate glass, these gloves, these robots: one might be in an atomic research laboratory. The terrible, the imperceptible atom is that instant at which, from robot to robot and through the thickness of all the glass in the world, the eye at last encounters the object (the *human* eye through all that lies between, the *human* object under all its disguises), that meeting-point, that divine judgment (since whoever he is, the novelist or the artist at this moment takes upon himself the role of God and is for this moment the disguise of God), that spark.

The more one takes precautions the more one emphasizes the importance of this act of writing, painting, composing, which *commits*, even if it is not committed; this view of life which judges even if it refuses the terms of judgment. And furthermore why should this moment of truth be kept for art alone? Why should the artist be the only one to have to come up to Léautaud's fine definition : "What is a writer, or what should he be? A man who weighs his words, not only before writing, but also before speaking . . ." Once a man makes use of words, why should he not be responsible for them?

At this point the subtlest novelist meets the most mystical of painters, and Huxley's delicately shaded precautions say neither more nor less that the rugged words of Van Gogh: "It is a wonderful thing to look at an object and to find it beautiful, and to keep it in your mind, and to say afterwards, I am going to set about drawing it; and then to work until it is reproduced." Yes. It is beautiful to look at an object, to become aware of it, to live it. But will not each man paint it in his own way? Will not the view of the object always be different and the judgment of it vary perpetually? No doubt.

But the effort is always the same. The confrontation is always the same. The acceptance is always the same. The relationship between the conscience, the talent, the whole being of Cézanne and of Van Gogh and their life; between Ghy's whole being and her life; between myself and my patient effort, and this book— always the same.

A living relationship, continually modified, continually changed by the broadening—or the shrinking—of the range of awareness. Always differing in your form, coefficient and range, and always the same lovely mathematical relationship : I do not wish to cheat or wriggle, and from now on I shall call you God.

PART THREE

So THERE WE ARE. The detective story is coming to an end. There are only a few pages left, and with a very natural satisfaction in our own penetration we hurry on to see the killer unmasked. We are going to be able to cry "I knew it all along! It was God who was the killer!"

It only remains for him to be arrested; a splendid passage describing his capture. It was on such and such a day, at such and such an hour, when suddenly . . . Soothed as we are by at last possessing the answer, we are ready to listen to the author, in order to know *how it ends*. The key, the master-word, has been given us, with its whole train of following words, its little robot-court, all of whose members wear the one same smile, like the courtiers of an absolute monarch. The essentials have been given. All that now has to be done is to make the deductions. The labels are ready; so is the pleased smile of those who have understood at last. "Oh, I see. I had not *placed* you . . ."

Nor had I, to tell you the truth: I had not *placed* myself. So it is done then? Nothing is left but to launch into about fifty very edifying pages, which will, of course, delight everyone. K., for example. I do not know him, but they tell me that he is not very fond of me, and I can make that out when I read him.

Tell him, "The murderer was God." He rejoices, snatches up his pen, plunges into analysis and deduction: untroubled by any scruples, she has gone from the shocking to the Catholic novel. Oh, it is quite cleverly aimed at the best-sellers list. At the rate of a novel every two years she can live comfortably. And in the dislike which K., for some obscure reason, feels for me, there will be a new ingredient—a certain warmth, something of that murky kindness that links the detective and the criminal who has 'squealed'. I have made his job easier; made my own condemnation easier; and he too feels a sort of gratitude to me for it. I am in the game—a game whose rules and jargon he knows. The confession has been recorded; I have given away my accomplice and nothing else counts: the murderer was God. Instant imprisonment.

And yet no. Between that day when I was a child and the great open door of a church first attracted me, between that day when I was an adolescent and I was first stirred by the sight of those bowed heads, and the day when the name of God, at once both old and new, returned to my lips, there had been great rich virgin expanses of thought, great expanses in which no doubt germination was going on, but going on in such oppressive darkness: and between that day when at last I thought (and perhaps supposed that this brought matters to a head): "From now on I shall call this relationship God", and that day in June when I was to walk under the dusty chestnut-trees of the avenue Latour-Maubourg towards a little chapel where I was expected, there was still to be a long sleep, a long-drawn-out task, and, perhaps, a long period of fear.

Why? To be sure, why this wasted time, this waiting, when it seemed that no more than a single step was needed to carry me over this frontier. Why? But also why the

first church?

Curiosity. Deep-rooted idleness of childhood. Distress, too. No doubt there were childish passions for someone in the same form, of course, or for that cold-eyed, elegant schoolmistress who would never have any notion of it at all. And to be sure in the evening, as I sat at a kitchen table (I have always loved kitchen tables) there was the sadness of the prospect of the little gardens, the roofs, the sadness of the cry of gulls; and the patient pencil between my fingers. But the anxiety, the distress, was already there; the words around me and perhaps even those absurd words that I was writing, those ridiculous words that passed one another like so many bright-coloured, gay, gleaming balloons in the sky, sometimes bursting (distress), but incurably separate from one another . . .

I wandered around the churches. The nearest was the ugliest: false Gothic crotchets, whose ugliness I was aware of—but ugliness, in short, was in the world, part of it; it was curious and even perhaps interesting. Machine-made stained glass, black and yellow walls, dripping with commonplaceness, ugly, light-coloured wooden doors, varnished, like the doors of a shop. The ponderous, commonplace crowd that came out of it, a crowd with hats on and gloves, a well-known and a ridiculous species of grown-ups—some of whom went (to church) and some of whom did not.

I went round the church; I approached it; that was all. Who could tell whether that everyday ugliness did not conceal the treasure of a key, an explanation. Only one thing was clear—the others, the grown-ups, were not in agreement. Some went, others did not. No questions, no torments. I waited until I should understand. Very patiently. It reminded me of the war. Some were pro-German; others not. There had been a time when everything seemed plain—those who 'had not been in favour' (of the Germans, of course) had won. For a certain time there were the 'evil' and the 'good'. That was agreed. One side (those who had won) put the others (some of them) in the lions' cages in the Antwerp zoo. It seemed odd to me.

But in one's childhood what quantities of odd things there are! What quantities of things there are whose explanation one must wait for! At least I was sure that the explanation would come one day. I was touchingly trustful.

It was odd that Julienne, the maid, whom I liked very much and who was beautiful, should have to remain shut up in the basement, where I was not to go *too often*. A shade of meaning. I was not forbidden to go into the kitchen. It was just a question of not going *too often*. A slight difference. I waited until I should understand. Patience and good will: I wanted to learn the idiom and know the rules of the game. I did not want to adventure myself into it without being sure what it was all about. I was rather afraid of the others (their ridiculousness) and of myself. There were moments when I was overcome by an incredible violence: I felt it as if it were a stranger, some other being that also inhabited my body. I was ready to come to terms with it, however. I wanted that it too should be made understandable, together with its directions for use.

Church, then. Another world. Shades of meaning too. "You will make your choice later," said my parents. They had made theirs: they did not go. Or did not go any more. Were they not certain of being right? They did not want to influence me: I should make my own choice. It was kind. I understood it. But how was I to choose? On the basis of what? Did one *choose* to be such and such a person (sometimes it appeared that one did: one either went to church or one did not; one was either pro-German or one was not); but did one choose to be in the basement or in the big oak-panelled dining-room, hung with Malines leather?

I was very fond of Julienne, and she was beautiful. But it was not right to talk to her *too much;* I was not to overdo it. There were also school friends whom I was not to see *too much* of. Suzanne, whose father was a hairdresser. For one afternoon we sold cosmetics in the shop. I should not have done it. Not that it was exactly *wrong*. It was one of those indefinable things that lie in that region of the absurd into which I was progressing carefully, with little cautious steps, very anxious to adapt myself, very willing to understand and to agree. But it was difficult. I wanted to be sure.

There were those men who gathered on certain days in the rue du Pélican—a street in which there were money-changers' and diamond merchants' shops. You would often see immense beards, rather long overcoats, black hats. Jews. Jews are not to be persecuted. It is *wrong*. The people who were pro-German persecuted the Jews. Atrocious. These men were quite obviously harmless. Their hats were a little strange. But in the rue du Pélican there were little 'Jewish' food shops where no doubt these men bought their provisions; and the translucid cucumbers were very tempting—so was the pink, rimed salmon and the gilded heap of rolls sprinkled with caraway-seeds.

And one should not linger in the rue du Pélican. Nor talk to any of these men (though one might bow, if it so happened that one had met him several times). I was very insistent that we should buy some of the cucumbers. Yes: it was possible; it could be done—but with the faintest hesitation, which threw as it were the faintest shadow of suspicion over the cucumbers (or on the men, or the black hats), so that one rather wanted to wash one's hands, and the pleasure of eating the cucumbers was subtly intermingled with this holding-back, this shadow of a shadow of reserve. Was one a Jew of one's own choice? While I was waiting to come to a decision upon this point I said to myself that if I were they, I should have avoided wearing the black hat, the rather high black hat that was a mark of the body to which they belonged. Later I found that not all did wear it. Well then?

Patience. Everything would become plain. The church. I went in. The statues were ugly too, their colours insipid: a woman was knitting at the table in the entrance, and she looked cross: pamphlets. It all looked thoroughly boring; but perhaps it had a meaning. My immense and patient curiosity. Patient, but hungering to do something that had a meaning, to understand, to live!

Wonderful childhood! Marvellous thoughtful age of twelve, age when understanding means living. How much you have to live, suffer and make mistakes before rediscovering the clearsightedness of twelve! Once I understood, I thought, everything would be settled. (And here I am, years later, I who have understood, and nothing is settled. A step, however, a single step, no more; and the whole of childhood thrusting me on from behind. But I hesitate and I am afraid. I was never afraid when I was a child.)

My little grandmother, frail, bent, lively, with the kindest face in the world under her banded hair—a style that she must have been shown (unless she saw it in a magazine and set herself to copying it, finding it fashionable) once and for all in about 1901 or perhaps 1895; and in her big black bag, as well as her knitting, a spotless handkerchief, some Vichy pastilles and a little bottle of melissa cordial (a panacea, indeed), she had a tin case with a little Saint Anthony in it, about an inch long or a little more; and several times a day, when she had lost something or other, she invoked the saint. This practice surprised me. My grandmother was very pious. People spoke of her piety kindly, with a shade of affectionate amusement, as of a fad natural in old ladies and one that was perfectly suitable for them. Fair enough. There were quantities of old ladies in church.

At Easter time the great neon cross blazed on the dismal façade. There were streamers that looked to me just like election posters : they said "Perform your Easter duty". There was also the cathedral, and that was an 'artistic gem' which people passing through were taken to see (and the Beguines' house at Bruges where, said my mother, one of my great-aunts died of cold). The black Virgin in the cathedral. Candles : silence. The pictures by Rubens, which the verger uncovered, solemnly drawing the green serge curtains. A particular attentive curiosity. The people who go into churches are Catholics.

I thought that no initiation could ever possibly turn one into a

Jew nor into a person who lived in the basement—these two species were linked in my mind, and I felt a special kindness for them, because of that vague injustice that hung over them and over all those whom it was better not to see *too often*. But from my grandmother I knew that it was possible to become a Catholic. And she also spoke of 'the *true* religion'. The burning fascination of the word truth. A magic operation and one would be in possession of the truth. The same as saying in possession of the world, thought I, at the wonderful age of twelve.

It depended on me alone. That choice, which my parents put off to some misty era (later, you will make your choice), was in fact the only one that I could make at once. My only freedom. A means of escaping from the world imposed upon me by my parents (I loved them : I only mean that this world was imposed in that I had not chosen it, that it seemed incomprehensible to me, and that I felt a stranger in it—though this did not in any way imply revolt). It was the only means I had of acting upon the world, of escaping from that bewildering gratuitousness that is imposed upon children.

An old, bowed priest, utterly devoted to the daily round. But still rather interested in the possibility of a secret conversion. In the evening, after school, on some excuse or other I got out and darted into the dark church, my heart thumping a little. My grandmother, my innocent accomplice, told her beads as one shells peas, in the lap of her black or grey dress. "And so your parents know nothing about all this," said the old priest, nodding. "It can be done, but . . . It might be said . . ." I had the feeling of being grown up at last. Confabulations . . . Then, "Obviously, a secret baptism, if you are sure you want it . . ."

Mysterious, magic ceremony. I thought about it. *And then what?* What did you feel, what did you turn into? I tried to detect marks of this mysterious initiation on the faces of those who came to see us. Nothing. Did my grandmother herself, apart from her way of calling upon Saint Anthony, show any engaging peculiarities? She was very kind. Nothing mysterious in that. People laughed a little, quite kindly, at her perpetual talk, her unceasing business—she never stopped tying up parcels, clicking her knitting-needles, worrying about railway time-tables, arranging drawers and the vast quantities of boxes that she possessed . . .

"If I baptize you, will you be able to go on practising the Christian virtues in the non-practising atmosphere in which you live?" he asked, scribbling something in a little notebook : he shut it with an elastic band. (He had already taught me a little of the terminology. "What is the Trinity?")

I felt strongly that I had to answer these questions and the others. I was in another set of gears, another mechanism, another vocabulary. But the absurd remained; and so did that feeling of being a foreigner there, of speaking a country's language whose rhythm one does not feel instinctively . . . Like a coward I said yes to his question, and he fiddled with his elastic. "Tell your grandmother and come at eight o'clock in the evening on the nineteenth," he said, with a worried look. Panic. I was no longer certain of anything. The sun-truth, the mirage-truth, was it *his* truth and nothing else at all? Was it indeed absolute? I insisted upon the absolute.

I did not keep the appointment. A suspicion hovered over it. Swapping some words for others—a ridiculous kind of trading. It may be simply that these conversations ended by boring me. My grandmother sighed; prayed to Saint Anthony. I was still twelve, thirteen, fourteen : never-ending ages. I set about falling in love with a person in a bookshop. He copied Rilke's letters and sent them to me, hardly altered. So between thirteen and fourteen-and-a-half I was in love with Rilke. I might have done worse. It was no longer truth that was the dazzling mirage. I dazzled myself, gently saying over and over again, "I am living . . . I am living." Adolescence, short, and like a thunder-stroke. Adolescence, which still had to go by way of that

American church

The lightning-quick transition from childhood to the 'adult' state : it goes so very fast! There is no link other than these words, these continual words on paper, and this perpetual effort, which is not yet a weariness, nor yet a headache, to find out which I should choose. I have never stopped writing for close on twenty years now. It is my unit of measurement.

Adolescence, then. I do not intend to linger over those wonderfully coloured noisy years, those years of fairs and sledges, those frightening years too, in which faces could suddenly become as fantastic as carnival masks, and as inhuman. And oneself in the middle of these colours as if one were in the middle of a prism, in the centre of a merry-go-round, at the centre of the world; and if this whirling stops now and then it is because all through everything one retains the habit of sitting down with the utmost regularity at a little table, wherever it may be, and of setting down words in a line, however hard it may be, words and yet more words . . .

No, I do not mean to describe those years. Just two words, to set that varnished pitchpine church (I have been told that that is its name), that very clean church with its 'discreet' neon lighting, in its context. Two words to reach that church. To reach it by way of those books I read, all those books which had already made their way through my fourteen-year-old head. Yes, my paper-filled head, indeed, crammed with words. An absurd world, but not a hostile one; a childish, pretty play, it appeared to me. The days passing faster: evening parties at home, which seemed to me an enchantment. My sister and I, barefoot on the staircase, watching for something that never happened. Sometimes, at the bottom of the stairs, a pair would go by, dancing, and vanish without seeing us.

Absurd, fascinating. I read *War and Peace*. I expected scenes, elopements; but I knew that there were no duels any more—such a pity! Sometimes a compassionate guest would bring us up a cake; and my fourteenth year having gone by, it appeared to me that the guest came up more readily. Cloud. But how I dreamed of those splendid evenings. Were they really splendid? In any case there was music and women wearing a great deal of scent: I read *Gone with the Wind* and I frantically admired one of my mother's friends, who had a very low-cut dress and a crowd of admiring men.

So that, in short, was what one wanted? Fifteen and a half, sixteen, and, wonder of wonders, I began to go out! The intoxication of a very unpretentious little white dress: young men ask me to dance, and having seen them twice it appears to me that they are extraordinarily slow in throwing themselves at my feet. I had just published—there had just been published for me—a collection of those poems made out of the long years of waiting, of childhood; but it was months since I had stopped writing verse.

Rilke was forgotten, and the poets; now it was novels that filled the long night sessions and the excited mornings; I thought of nothing but dancing and then of dancing again, and at last (at last! I was already feeling almost old) a charming man kissed me in a cloakroom. I loved him, obviously. I loved him for a week, and afterwards I was very proud of being his mistress, and there you are. I was a grown-up, without thereby having stopped being a child. For when my parents found out and were furious, it seemed to me *monstrously* unfair! And yet that too was in the novels. But I had imagined, from people's way of speaking, their asides and their little smiles, that this was one of the sort of things you joke about. Somewhere I must have got things wrong. Or else people were just not logical; for I felt very distinctly that I should find nobody to stand up for me. And there I was packed off to America, like a scandalous and embarrassing parcel.

I wept, for that was my personal logic; I wept for I loved: and still applying a mathematical logic I determined to get married as quickly as possible, so as to 'set myself free'. How one falls into one's own trap, how one undeceives oneself, how one finds oneself in Paris again, just eighteen, pregnant by one, in love with another, married, divorced, wonder-struck by a brand-new and charming baby one does not know how to handle, and how in the end, in spite of having received a few bangs in the struggle, one makes the best of it quite cheerfully, because no doubt that is what life is like and what is the point of beating one's brains about it— all that is another story.

American churches are as ugly as our ugly churches. That is the point I wanted to reach.

But what lovely priests the Americans have! This one is fair-haired, athletic, absolutely made for the films. He has a tooth-paste smile and he exhales a scent of menthol and brilliantine. "Come, you must not be afraid of me!" he says, with great cordiality. A poor district of New York: little houses zig-zagged with fire-escapes. Since that first experience of mine I avoid churches. I know that there are people with set ideas inside them; people who would condemn me. I do not admit that they are right. But with a South Sea island superstition I make a cast about to avoid these people, to avoid even the place in which they fore-gather. Prudence. You never know. It needs only a trifle for people (parents, for instance) to turn into judges.

Sometimes by night I dream about this transformation. Distress. Always the semantic distress. What was there, in the way my parents and their friends spoke, to make one think that they would feel a genuine indignation at my 'misconduct'? Nothing. Well then? But I am no longer in quest of a logical process. I have gone beyond logic; or logic is for later on—it does not much matter which. What I am suddenly attracted by is these heads all bowed together, these voices all joined together, these faces.

I love people, the world, everything, this afternoon on Fourth Avenue, right at the far end of it, where there are ugly houses slashed with fire-escapes, and my little room not far from the vibrating elevated railway; and the drugstore and the dubious restaurant (they exist even in America; and this one, which pretends to be French, has the brilliant idea of calling itself *Le Petit Coin*), and the smells of frying and medicines (there is a pharmaceutical laboratory quite near)—I love it all, this rather empty summer evening (still bright with a rosy sky, but already here and there the spitting of the neons as they light up), and I love feeling myself, free from everything, free from nothing, free, for example, to go and see this amiable American priest, who insists upon my calling him Fred.

"What is a little sin?" says Fred to me. "It is a spot on a jacket. You wash it and there you are. Join the church!"

It is one way of looking at things. One way of speaking of them. But what about deciding whether some given object of consideration is a spot or not? "But it is written down!" he cries indignantly. "It is in here!" He taps a book bound in beige plastic. Clearly, if it is written down, that is very convenient. I do not dislike the idea; but from the practical point of view . . . And then there must be other books.

As I said, I am no longer at the stage of logic.

"And what do you have to do, once you belong to the church?"

"Why . . . get married, have children, work, improve yourself . . ."

"Is that all?"

"And be a good citizen," says Fred.

His smell of brilliantine! His flashing smile! His well-fed calmness!

It was a neo-Gothic church with a 'Renaissance' pulpit made of pine. I never went back.

That was not the moment for logic or for enthusiasm. That was not the moment for meaningful words, nor for impetuous outbursts, nor for delight in living and the direction of it along given channels. Not at that juncture. Profit and loss. Let us think about something else. That question that has been filling my mind and that has begun to be very alarming for the past fortnight, for example. Surely it is not possible that I, still so close to childhood, should in my turn be with child? No, that is not logical either. But morning-sickness does not obey the mind's imperatives, and it forces me to change the subject-matter of my thoughts. Fortunately I have always liked babies.

This time it is good-bye for a long while. Good-bye to inquiry and reflection, good-bye to the very name of anxiety (it is still there, but now it gives itself pretexts and grown-up names), good-bye to patience and impatience, and to rebellion and to causeless distress, and to the innocent wiles that hunt down everyday words. Yes, farewell the inquiry: perhaps it is that which is childhood's end? There remains the splendid pure violence that has its own private logic. Still and always there remains the old habit, so old that I no longer even know its beginning, of writing. That habit which, going on steadily morning after morning from one morning to another, was to lead me to the point when just a moment ago I wrote the words, 'From now on I shall call you God.'

And then what a triumph! What clarions, what trumpets! Noël, Noël, and the bells ringing out, and the grave slowing down of the pen over the paper that has turned into parchment, and the gold and the azure of that book (and all the K.s in this world put to silence, for there is no answer to the name of God; and the great Catholic novelist, who puts it into everything he touches, even election pamphlets, is perfectly aware of the fact), and the lovely pictures which are slowly leafed through and which yield up their secret . . . How I should like to write that book in which everything becomes plain, that book in which everything is made clear, that book that I should have liked to read when I was a child. That book where every picture has underneath it *This is what it means*. And I believed that I could write that book. I even chose its title, though I always find titles so difficult. I should have called it *acrobatic moralities*

Why? One day I was at the carnival in a little village in Flanders. There was to be a torchlight parade and dancing in masks on the uneven stones of the little square. I had come early, rather before sunset. People were hurrying in the streets; the square was empty; now and then a masked person went by, furtively, as if still ashamed, and vanished round the corner of an alley. A very strange disguise, with its enormous cardboard head and tight clothes, strange in the same way that the mediaeval houses were strange under the violent make-up of the neon lights. Everyone was waiting for the moment when they should all rush out of their houses together and into the square, a sudden motley throng.

There was that feeling of waiting that comes before holidays; and in the air the smell of hasty frying, while the cafés were filled with the thick smoke of pipes and the sound of clashing glasses and saucers, and over everything there was a very slight anxiety, or tension. I was sitting in the middle of this smoke, and I had something of the feeling of being in a station. It was a small café, with a low ceiling : thick beams with Coca-Cola advertisements hanging from them, little green window-panes, broken-springed imitation-leather benches, and the men standing at the wooden counter (I observed that it was not plated) slapping one another on the back and roaring with perhaps slightly exaggerated laughter and good-fellowship.

There were some cardboard masks in a corner, put down in a heap on the ground, harmless as yet. On the shelves above the bar there were bunches of paper flowers under glass domes, unsophisticated and old-fashioned, and as I had seen flowers of the same kind in my grandfather's house I knew that they were archery prizes. The faded red and the ingenuous blue of the primitive flowers made me think of Epinal and its lead soldiers, red-cheeked lovers one dreams of at the age of twelve. I was thinking 'Epinal' and a little grey man came in, carrying an iron hoop and making a collection in a Martini ashtray.

It was a strolling tumbler, or to be more exact, a contortionist. He had neither a dog nor a goat, and his tired, dispirited look gave no great promise for the coming entertainment. Yet since they were waiting, the people made a circle, pulled back a few chairs and a table. We were right next to him.

He stood on his head, without any particular skill. He folded his legs backwards. He raised one arm and thrust his legs into the little iron hoop. He put his hand on the ground again and brought his legs farther over until they hid his face. Then the face reappeared a little higher up, between the calves; a grey face, devoid of expression. There was nothing particularly remarkable about this contortion other than the slowness and the kind of solemnity with which it was carried out. However, the men standing round (already slightly affected by their wine or their beer) were getting ready to clap heartily when the grey, round, flat head which was framed between the two legs and which we saw upside-down, opened its mouth and, in a grating Flemish that seemed to me to be archaic but which was perhaps no more than the dialect of another region, tonelessly uttered a little verse that may be translated thus:

> When my nimble frame I thus arrange,
> Why should it seem to you so strange?
> Most of the world is in this pass,
> Their heads right here in place of their arse.

The people laughed, without understanding very clearly; they laughed because of the rude word. The little man was quite unmoved by this success. With the same slowness his head pushed its way farther between his legs, his outstretched arms followed through the iron hoop and he suddenly took on the appearance of a kind of little parcel tied up by this unbelievably narrow bind-

ing, with his head, arms and legs coming through the small opening, while in spite of his teetering balance the contortionist, with
the same gravity, pronounced these doggerel lines :

> Neither arm nor leg can I move at all
> A piteous state in which to fall;
> But when a woman or money you see,
> You are in the very same state as me.

This acrobatic feat was generally held to be better than the
first. The verses surprised people; but they were not thought to
be a bad thing. I do not remember what he did afterwards. The
rhymes were tolerably dirty, if not downright obscene: their
coarseness increased and contributed much to their success. Like
everybody else, I put some money in the ashtray.

The little man bowed and went slowly off, with a tired and
gloomy air. He was offered a glass of gin. In his dull voice he
refused; for, as he told us (it was certainly a dialect that he was
speaking), alcohol gave him cramps in the stomach and prevented
him from doing his act. Looking out of the window I saw him go
into another café on the square, with his little iron hoop in his
hand. I wondered who had given him the idea of this strange act,
who had taught him the rhymes or had inspired them. No doubt
he had added a fair number of his own brand of jokes, but it
seemed to me that he would never have been able entirely to
invent this illustrating of his contortions.

The echo of Epinal in my mind (brought about by the café's
faded bunches of flowers) led me to think of Bruegel's series of
proverbs. It was an old Flemish tradition, one that I loved dearly,
that had turned up again here, perhaps by mere chance; and
suddenly that quite simple idea of the apparently obvious, but in
fact complex, relationship between picture and caption that had
been haunting me was exemplified. And what a lovely title! Acrobatic moralities!

By what I might call a stroke of fate (but not a revelation: or else an inexplicable, mysterious revelation, rather too surrealistic for my liking, although I very fairly recount it) on one idle Sunday, a vacation in the true sense of the word, I was taking one of the children round the museum of folk arts and traditions, and hanging on the wall I found an engraving that fascinated me. On yellowed paper, divided into little squares with their sides about three or four inches long, there were the postures of a tight-rope walker who was making use of a hoop for his contortions. And under these apparently commonplace pictures there were quatrains in old Flemish, many of which I could not understand; but what I could make out clearly showed that the intention, edifying or comic, was to establish a relationship between the attitudes and the ideas. Could any sign be clearer? I had to write the book, paint these scrupulously careful miniatures, these or others, and with that ingenuous confidence of the illuminators of a former age or of the present-day Soviet authors, write underneath: *This is what it means.*

Acrobatic moralities . . . I must bring them out again, all those images that surround me, all the dusty oddments that one has already accumulated by the time one is thirty: a quick flap with a duster and spread them out like a pack of cards. Give them the mysterious charm, the ambiguous poetry, of tarot cards—the *Wheel of Fortune*, the *Well*, the *Coil-Winding Conveyor-Belt*, the *Postman's Palace*, the *Fighting Women* . . . So there are my cards. And to each picture its own very simple, very plain meaning.

And the relationship between these pictures and these captions, 'I shall call it God from now on'. What a programme! And what a fascinating book to write! All these little revelations piling up and leading on to the great revelation—God. Beautiful pictures, full of pith, all the more beautiful for having a meaning!

Tunis, for example: landscapes, picturesque characters, Luc, the Goya-like fight of the women, and that first axiom, 'Thinking is already taking sides'. Or the *Coil-Winding Conveyor-Belt*, which is a splendidly modern setting and the beautiful machines that I should like to describe, with their steely weight and the weight too of those movements, those light triangles, hexagons that the labour of the factory-girls draws in the air: *value is a proportion*.

Or, more simply, the moment at Renée's party when we were all delighted by the beautiful Charente glasses. My thoughts upon that evening would have come first; and in a fine lyrical passage I should have asked myself, "But where have they gone, the real Renée, the real Clo, Etienne, Jean . . ." Perhaps I would have expressed a doubt (doubt is a capital thing for suspense); did this truth, the object of my inquiry and of my longing, really exist? Could it be conveyed? Had my inquiry, my work, any meaning? Rather sadly I should have noted the false, conventional language they all spoke, in which nothing tallied with anything; and then suddenly the miracle, a mathematical miracle suitable to me, the truth would have burst forth in the form of the felicitous proportions of the Charente glasses, the single, frail link between all these carefully hedged characters, shut up in themselves—the unanimous recognition of a truth, a truth whose existence was evident to all, the simple and almost commonplace beauty of these peasant glasses: a positive *Communion of the Saints*.

Joy, joy, tears of joy. And the moment when Renée showed me the white vase set there in front of the ochre wall in its own place, its only possible yet obvious place. That day I told myself that that was what grace must be, that ability and desire to make out one's own place in this colourless life, however humble the place might be (but why should it be humble? A little higher, a little lower, somewhat to the right or to the left—what has the idea of humility got to do with it?) and to do one's utmost to reach it.

I might go so far as to tell myself that it is not essential to make certain of this place. The effort alone is enough, since it acknowledges the existence of the place, and grants the architecture of the world.

Everything mingles with delight in making a Triumph of Truth built up like a painted ceiling, and by way of putting in a touch of elegance I go back to the Grillon, conjure up Marcel B. and explain that what vexes me in Marcel when he talks about me is not that he gets it wrong but that he does not mind whether he gets it wrong or not. All he wants to do is to dress up the world, and me, in a becoming garment—to create a fine-looking image, without troubling about whether it has any meaning.

That is not the sort of person we are; not at all. Nothing in our hands, nothing in our pockets. We shall explain everything, justify everything, and our book, *Acrobatic Moralities*, will have the staggering architecture of a cathedral. All that we lack at present is the topmost piece, the building's crown, the thing that is called the conclusion. But take care: do not go and spoil it all. The truth of the matter is that our life, at this point that we have reached, the point at which we triumphantly cried "God is the murderer," also lacks a conclusion, a seal, a stamp. It must be admitted that as yet we are no more than a sympathizer. We have not yet joined, we are not yet card-carrying members of the party: to put it plainly, we are not baptized. "Come into the church," said Fred, speaking out of his cloud of hair-oil. We did not go in. On the threshold, yes, and as close as possible. But that step, the only step that still has to be made (that step which would be the crowning-piece of the building and the conclusion of our book), was one that we did not make, however.

To speak quite frankly, there were some cards that had slipped in among the brilliant tarot pack—cards which prevented the patience from coming out. Deceitful cards, ambiguous images, portents of the anguish that I should have to exorcize before *looping the loop*, if indeed I managed to do it. Splendidly-named images, such as that one which I call

the mystery of the emerald

At the time when I read this tale (it was in an old volume of

La Semaine de Suzette, I think; but I can no longer be sure, although I can still smell the sourness of the paper) I took pleasure in lying with neither rhyme nor reason. It was the equivocal pleasure of being believed. Or else the half-conscious feeling that the scoldings I received for having lied would teach me the 'truth' —for me truth was, as it were, a person who was there, but hidden.

My parents' great kindness made everything worse. If I had felt any degree of enmity on their part I should have rebelled, and it would all have been quite simple. But there was none. This particular kind of distress or anxiety made me laugh and say all sorts of ridiculous things. When I was five or six I invented a little brother, who lived in Switzerland.

Then one day came and I was suffering from 'intercostal neuralgia'. I really did feel pain. But thanks to this pain I also took the opportunity of getting out of the lessons that bored me— gymnastics, drawing, grammar. I said that I was ill and they let me go down to the basement, where there was a deck-chair installed for the use of those who might go sick. It stood in a broad, dark, silent corridor; and down there sounds were muffled and distant. It was warm, because of the school's boiler, which was in a cellar close at hand and whose peaceful rumbling I could hear.

A teacher, distrustful of this gloomy, solitary place in which I was day-dreaming, came down to question me. "So you are not feeling well?" She was not convinced. Yet I had a strong feeling that she was not sure of herself; and I was armoured by the fact that I really was in pain.

"Oh, it will pass off," I said.

"Do you often feel ill like this?"

"Yes, often."

I could see that she was puzzled, leaning there over my chair, looking at me intently. She was a very tall woman; her features were hard, but full of kindness, and she had grey hair, done up in a severe bun. I was really fond of her. I was amused, but without any hostile nastiness, at the sight of a grown-up person being attacked by the ridiculous doubt that I, for my part, suffered from continually. There was no enmity in my attitude towards her.

"You don't like grammar?" she asked.

"Oh, it's all right," I said, with no great enthusiasm. A more vigorous protest would have been suspect.

How obvious it was that she did not know what to believe! This grown-up, so conversant with infinitives, participles, demonstrative pronouns, stood there, leaning over me; she did not know, and she had no power whatever over me that would enable her to know the truth. With a kind of wonder I told myself that she would never know whether I was really in pain. She could do what she liked, but I was dug in within myself, completely under cover, and she had no means whatever of coming at the truth.

The notion filled me with peace, and this mingled with the peace of the corridor. I did indeed feel myself completely sheltered, entirely at my ease, while she inspected me at length, severely, from her full height, for now she was standing up.

It was then that the tale I had read in *La Semaine de Suzette* came into my mind—the *Mystery of the Emerald*, in which some Englishmen with foolishly kind faces shook an Indian guide to make him say where he had hidden the Emerald that he had stolen. The guide was called Lakdar Mokri, and I had the tenderest of feelings for him (a little later Louis XI was to take his place in my heart, which was always ready to beat for the unfortunate), and with a horrible grin (though in my imagination I provided him with a high degree of nobility, thus rectifying what I conceived as the artist's prejudiced view of his features) he declared, "You may have my life, but you shall never have my secret." I had liked this part of the tale; I had liked it more than the end, where the 'good' Englishmen (why good? Since these archeologists had filched the Emerald from the forehead of a composite Buddha) got back their Emerald and made a present of it to the

British Museum, while the unfortunate Lakdar was eaten by a sacred crocodile.

"You may have my life, but you shall never have my secret," I said slyly to myself, while she stood there dominating me with her height, her look and her sovereign powers as a schoolmistress. Yet towards her I felt none of the hatred that Lakdar Mokri directed towards the pink-faced Englishmen—on the contrary, I was quite fond of her. It was the school that I did not like, the school that I thought ridiculous and boring. I was paying its absurdity back with more absurdity, that was all.

And the pain which dug into my ribs was almost pleasurable because I could say to myself that even if her examination led her to believe that I was only pretending to feel unwell, she would be wrong. The ambiguity of the truth amused me. I *was* ill, *but* I thought grammar a bore. She could never come to a conclusion, possibly. She could stay there all the morning, but she would not have 'my secret'. And in fact she stayed there for a while, saying nothing. As for me, I was completely shut in, wholly armoured, impregnable, almost dozing in my calmness, and I still felt no kind of tension whatever. Suddenly she gave up; it seemed to me that she uttered a sigh, and she went away.

I almost wanted to call her back : I was fond of her, indeed I was, and although there was slyness in my refusal to talk there had been no enmity or contempt. I had reversed the roles, that was all. Instead of being a child surrounded by absurdity, inscrutable words and bodies, I had made myself into an adult, master of the words and meanings, a wayward demiurge, an ironical and mysterious statue. It was a game. But she had sighed. I should have liked to call her back and explain : I would explain one day—I would explain that evening.

Then it had occurred to me that she might not believe me. The warm, dreamy peace in which I had been swimming suddenly left me. I sat up on the edge of the deck-chair. Everything was still the same—the silence and the dimness, the remote sound of cars, the wheezing of the boiler, the drone of children mumbling something. But the safety was no longer with me. Once more I thought of the words of the guide that had pleased me so, ". . . but you shall never have my secret." If he had given his secret away, might not the Englishmen have disbelieved him? If I were to speak to Mlle M. might she not believe that I had not felt unwell at all? Or again would she still be in doubt? And anyhow, since she had just found it impossible to know what I was really thinking and feeling, would it not be impossible for me too to know what she really thought of my advance? This very simple reflecion quite overwhelmed me. The delightful feeling of calmness that I had experienced in this corridor, this chair, this warm twilight had suddenly turned into an agonizing feeling of loneliness, no longer chosen, but inflicted. Everything had altered. I did not go to see Mlle M. Furthermore, I forgot the whole thing for years: only the vague distress remained, hovering over dark and ill-defined matters. I tore up the numbers of *La Semaine de Suzette* which had the tale of the Emerald. That was all.

The sudden change of my deliberate solitude: it turned from a refuge into a prison. The sudden change of the words: their freedom turned into slavery. The charm of the absurd became the anguish, the anxiety, of the absurd. Equivocal change, disconcerting metamorphosis: the Emerald was a disturbing image. It made me think of those tales in which, because of a fairy's spell, the words uttered by the good sister turn into roses as they leave her mouth, while the inevitable bad sister's become snakes. What would the words that I was going to *give* life become? Refuge or prison? Roses or serpents? One step, one single step, and these words would no longer be content to remain words: they would insist upon being made flesh. I should no longer be their mistress, I should not choose them—it would be they who would choose me. I should no longer name God, but God would name me: and who knows what would become of me then?

I had long since known this power that words possessed once

they had been said. I revered it. I dreaded it; and sometimes I tried to laugh at it, as one does when one is too frightened. At this period, long, long before the day God was caught red-handed in the act of omnipresence, I tried a little tale, a kind of fable (a fable already) in which the words, those little lares, played a mischievous part. I called this fable

the engagement-book

Let us say a woman. Let us say a woman of thirty-five. Date of birth in her passport, which is hidden by an elegant leather case. Let us say seven in the morning by the little travelling-clock, which is hidden by an elegant leather . . . Let us say a car, a flat, a career, an engagement-book which is hidden by an elegant . . . Let us say too much leather, too many clocks and engagement-books altogether. This woman wakes up.

When a woman like Lise wakes, does she think of her lover, her office or her hairdresser? Is it a pleasant waking or an anxious one? Quick or slow? No doubt it is calm. Everything has been ready since the evening before, the kettle ready on the gas, the tea-pot and the sugar-bowl on the tray, a glass of orange-juice in the refrigerator. And on the bedside table, concealed by its elegant leather binding, her engagement-book.

It is clear that when Lise wakes up she thinks of her engagement-book. Now she lost it yesterday evening, between eight and nine o'clock, in the Place des Ternes, as she was saying good-bye to a friend; and while she was looking for the keys of her car the engagement-book, in which she had just written down an appointment, must have slipped . . . Now, vexed, she remembers, at something past seven . . . A glance at the clock: not going. Forgot to wind it yesterday evening, although I never . . . I who am so exact . . . I already had the feeling that there was something missing, and I thought that that argument with Jean . . . Absurd: it was the engagement-book. God knows what time it may be now.

A look at the window : sunbeam; pale, no doubt, but a sun-beam. God knows what time . . . and since the day is spoilt any-how, perhaps a walk in the Bois . . . No. My engagements. And no time (maybe) to do my exercises! She agitatedly throws back her blankets, and something falls hard. Oh, my spectacles! It is too much altogether.

Quite at a loss. The time and the place of her appointments flee before her beautiful short-sighted eyes. And what to put on when you don't know who you are going to see? Business-woman, fashionable woman, simple and sporting type, a woman—practi-cally a girl—with a phoney peasant checked handkerchief on her head? What can you choose to be, without your engagement-book? Hesitation waltz in front of the hanging-cupboard. What does she own, Lise, thirty-five years old, dark? She wanted to go on the stage, then did not; then window-dressing, displays, and lastly advertising, which is her career; and a little flat in the rue des Arts-et-Métiers, done up with taste. She entertains her friends there on Fridays and Sundays, and her mother once a year in the little next-door room, which was once a maid's room but which now has running water in it.

For her mother she dresses extravagantly—that immense hat swathed in tulle, those pink satin trousers, all the sort of things you buy in a moment of enthusiasm and dare not wear afterwards. She is Lise X; she goes to her office at whatever time she chooses and she comes home when she likes, eats anything she wants—mostly grapefruit—and Jean finds himself ringing her up ten times a day in an English accent (it is very commonplace, but it is enough to convince Mme X).

But is Mme X going to come? Lise has blue-jeans and a set of checked shirts (very amusing, as they say in shops) to paint a room in the flat, or potter about a bit or do the washing-up after a little youthful dinner with some particular friends; she has some broken check and dark flannel suits for the office (with various dodges for lightening and 'making them young', innumerable dodges ranging from leather revers that can be taken off to an organza jabot which can be carried in a plastic bag and added to the suit to make it right for a cocktail party).

Lise wearing a flannel skirt, a cashmire twin-set, 'invisible' lipstick and a gold chain round her wrist, takes on the air of a stern young officer, just a little perverted—an air that suits her better than the little-girl look, the upper lip raised, that goes with her checked shirts. And the 'not very formal dinner' bottle-green velvet dress turns her into a romantic young woman with a plump bosom and a false bun, immeasurably gentle, attentive to the elderly man (Pierre) who will marry her one day. But her black and Victorian eye is heightened with a touch of perversity (Arden pencil: nine francs) if Jean is one of the party, and in that case the bottle-green bosom is garnished with false white underwear which a false button lets out in a cascade—a falsely innocent cascade, of course—which prepares the way for the 'schoolgirl' nightdress that Lise will wear during the 'night with Jean'.

When she is alone she wears pyjamas very much in the style 'strong cigarette on waking'. But she has not smoked anything at all this morning because *she has lost her engagement-book*.

Cannot choose what to wear, cannot choose a make-up: does not know the time! One way of getting out of it—do nothing; pretend to have flu. That is all right for the office. But what about the other engagements? Jean, ten o'clock at the Rotonde? I'll walk there. And since I am not going to work, a spring frock with a petticoat, a big wicker-work hand-bag (perhaps the swimming-pool), pink and blue make-up, the scent that Jean prefers; it is rather saccharine, but . . .

Now she has left the flat. At the café, disaster! It is Marc! The appointment was with Marc! Marc-childhood-friend, turtle-neck-Marc, Marc-gauloise-bleue, poster-sticker, Marc-the-buddy, Marc-the-stop-press-intellectual (Marc-Marienbad today). Marc, of all God-awful blunders!

"Have you dressed up like that for me?"

His pebble-glasses (why not?): the talk gets off on the wrong foot—De Gaulle and *Les Temps Modernes* are absurd in this flowered print. And this scent! She has a go at the under-developed nations but it does not answer; the sun, and this basket . . .

"What are all these flowers on your dress?"

Wondering, admiring gaze; childhood memories. They will go to the swimming-pool. Really, you know, he dives better than Jean; and without his spectacles . . . Kiss.

"Tomorrow, at five o'clock."

"I have lost my engagement-book."

He gives her his, the *Lettres Françaises* engagement-book.

"Darling!"

Back to the little flat. Horrified: quick, a cashmire twin-set—green? No, grey, severe, severe; the chain-bracelet, hair smooth; the scent went off in the swimming-pool, thank God. A quick lunch at the snack-bar and I shall go to the office and see if somewhere or other I have not jotted down . . .

At the snack-bar, Jean.

"Well, you were in no hurry: and how severe you look!"

"Jean, you are a bore, and where are those fried eggs? I look how I want to look, and . . ."

"You might as well say right out that . . ."

"All right, then, I shall. I am sick of living like this. At my age a woman needs something besides . . ."

"So it was in order to tell me that that you dressed yourself like a nun?"

"If you like to think so . . ."

"This is it, then? You are showing me the door? I must say you are not very civil about it: when you are going to break, the decent thing to do is to arrive on time."

"I had forgotten that . . . my engagement-book . . ."

"That beats everything."

Gone. She lights a strong cigarette with a manly and determined gesture.

There is no doubt about it : this is a break. And why not? What
do things depend on? If I had put on the green twin-set, perhaps
. . . It can't be helped.

At the office, masses of people. Of course, a cocktail-party being
given for . . . She had suggested it herself, by way of giving a
literary or artistic excuse for those evening parties which . . . Pierre
Melchior: no, not a chief, but a friend who . . .

"I really don't mean to talk clothes to you, my dear; but those
boy-scout garments at a cocktail-party are positively . . ."

Everybody has gone. The cigarette-ends on the carpet have
vexed him and he is cross at not seeing the lustre of young breasts
in the green velvet dress, the black head-band, the false bun, the
submissive gentleness of the Elizabeth Arden eye . . . Not even
made up!

"I dress as I like . . . What a way to speak to anyone!"

"But after all . . . The people you see for the firm—Marc
Lauriol?"

"Well, yes : I happen to go to the swimming-pool sometimes . . .
a free woman . . ."

"One is allowed to make a remark, I believe."

"With a political slant?"

"Why not?"

"The Algerian war . . ."

"Three months' warning for the cadres."

She goes home in a rage by the underground. Crowds, smells,
dust. Exhausted. A brown tweed overcoat in the hall, very good
quality, very ugly. Mother! "Here I am, darling. Dear me, how
dreadful you look!"

The mac, the rumpled twin-set, the colour drained from her
face by tiredness, her eyes burning with anger, Lise is a thirty-five-
year-old shorthand-typist or the underfed child who 'won all the
prizes'.

"Flu. I'm sure it's flu."

"Go to bed darling : I will see to everything."

Bed; pyjamas : Lise shivers. Old flannel dressing-gown miraculously found again. And, oh yes, tisane ! The flat is filled with the
smell of stewed apples. That engagement-book ! Tomorrow,
swathed in organza, will she break with Marc? Gently she
breathes in the smell of the blanket, pulled up to her face—a
childhood habit. "There is my little Lise again . . ." Oh! Send
Mother to the rue des Morillons, first thing tomorrow morning.

I never was able to write that fable. I took it up from time to
time, and I freshened some of the details—the new franc took the
place of the old, the Algerian war that of the war in Indo-China
. . . No good. And yet I really did like that clattering, that clashing, that absurd disorder, that uprooting that affects every
moment and every thought in Paris, where the only thing that
gives your mind, your incessantly battered, battering, banging
mind that hurries about like a ball on a pin-table, some kind of
a foothold is the engagement-book, the watch, the label hastily
stuck on to every face and every feeling.

But Lise . . . no, there was something wrong there. These whis-
kies, swimming-pools, offices that you go to when you choose . . .
The girl irritated me. Not because she did not exist : far from it.
Because she existed only too much, or in too many copies, like the
dress that you stop wanting because you see it every time you walk
down the street. Go thoroughly into her, analyse her, of course.
But these dolls with soft permanent waves always have the same
thing inside them; it is always the same touching discovery—the
menstruation-calendar next to the teddy-bear, and the good old
marriage-lines, already tied up with a blue ribbon, under the slips
from the weighing-machine. It is really quite impossible.

So much the worse for the words. In the same way Jean's story
is impossible—Jean, who married an ugly wife because he believed that virtue meant always doing what you most dislike.

Still, there is a charming moment in this story (to be handled lightly, in the Diderot manner: lumps in cynical throats); the moment at which Jean becomes aware that his wife is not as ugly as all that, that she is not even ugly at all, and sets about falling in love with her; and a tragi-comical and Freudian moment (one never hears about Freud's comic side and this is a great mistake: there are times when he rivals Courteline. When he tells the story of a woman who suffers from constipation, for instance: prompted by the psycho-analyst the husband brings her a bunch of flowers one evening; the woman, magically set free from her torment, darts in the direction that you have guessed, and the joyful sound of rushing water marks the end of this misunderstanding between husband and wife)—the Freudian moment, then, when from fear of love or of enjoying himself, which is quite as bad (I will say no more), he averts his gaze from his newly-beautiful wife and hurls himself upon the downright hideous mistress he takes as a form of penance.

It is this perpetual question of words' malpractice, once they are allowed the upper hand. Jean thought the word virtue better than the word love and it never occurred to him to crack the nut of their meaning: may it not have been that the kernel was the same? He preferred breaking his teeth.

But I shall not tell this story. Possibly because it is just rather too obvious? The caption has eaten up the picture; there is nothing left but the words. Sterility. From that day when the caption became God, no more bells, no more splendid capital letters, no more tears of joy. A long torpor follows, an incomprehensible sterility. An everlasting *what then*? A waiting, a fear; and what is worse, a revolt.

what then?

Daniel, eleven years old, listens to an Aznavour record called *Après l'amour*. He shrugs and says, "It's stupid. What does he think that means, after love? You either love people or you don't love them. There's no *after* love . . ." A child's dream; a wonderful, untrustworthy longing.

Once I had longed for God I did not want there to be an afterwards. The step that was still to be taken was vast and minute, everything and nothing at all. As Saint John says, the thinnest thread holds a bird to the ground just as well as the heaviest chain. I did not want the thread to break. The anguish of the void, of open space: and then, why move? There is no *after* love . . .

Paralysis. The mind blocked. And the body: muscles contracted as far as they will go, to such a pitch that writing feels like carrying out some labour requiring great physical strength. Strength: with all my strength I oblige my pen to move over the paper. My writing becomes more and more legible (with me this is a very bad sign); the words grow heavier; the themes stiffen into little pictures, demonstrations, anatomical morsels: it is impossible to bring them to life even for myself! Oh, it is not a question of writing well or badly, of communicating, nor of writing pure and simple: I can no longer manage to get through to myself. I look at myself, I shake myself—nothing comes. Fear, I tell myself. But fear can be thought, given a name. And agony was alive. This panic is a kind of sleep. So do something, God! Is it not enough to bear witness to you, to point you out at every street-corner, to turn every book into a kind of riddle "Where is the good Jehovah hidden?" so that when it is turned round your beard is always to be discovered in a corner.

Well then? And my arithmetical rule, my patience, my rather heavy carefulness—"What does this mean? What is the meaning of that?"—does it all go for nothing, then? And what about my service record, the church when I was a child, my enthusiasms at sixteen, my wild or foolish loves (they say you like that—the agony, I mean . . .), and then love itself, and work that grows harder every day. All these stages, these cross-checks, additions and headaches; and when after all that I put my trumpet to my lips and, worn out by so much effort, I roar *God* so loud that it splits their ears, you tell me that you decline to do your proper share? Revolting ingratitude.

For after all, what is it that I am asking you for? Happiness, fame, money, glory? None of these things. Nothing more than a final term. An end. Something that will let me go on to another exercise. A stop, a simple full-stop: an unpretentious punctuation. And then to be allowed to leave this table, and to go off for a stroll before starting on another theme (in which, of course, I am ready to leave you your rightful place—honour where honour is due).

Yet no. As far as punctuation went it was points of suspension that came to me, a question-mark, a comma. And God-comma is infinitely less impressive than God!!! You are all square with your conscience after three exclamation-marks. After a comma, no. I grew stubborn about this comma. I went to sleep over it. The only solution was flight, escape, a rope made out of sheets (has the beauty of this symbol been thoroughly appreciated?) In short,

a little lyricism

Symbolic figures, images, stories. Nothing obvious in what I am going to write, setting God down there like a boundary-stone. I wrote—a cry of revolt—God is not a theme! No, something else. Shapes of women, of course. Shapes of springs or fountain-heads, covered with moss, the face eroded, already part of that mystery of water and stone, which means that they are not merely women and symbols but already self-sufficient objects, secret objects, crowned with a beauty that is not mere meaning—what rest and peacefulness!

Two images, two like and unlike forms. Will they betray me? They were not chosen to act as witnesses: *where were you at such and such a time on such and such a day?* They were picked out as it were by chance, but an unavoidable chance: other forms that I might easily call up are there, lurking in the shadows, and they do not want to come out. One must certainly take advantage of those that will come out and show themselves in the light, submitting to the least organized of crystallizations, but perhaps the most revealing. I expect that this submission to nature will produce a kind of revelation. May it not be that the picture and the caption will merge once more in a secret harmony like the voice of the spring? Let that voice soothe us for a little. Let us be born.

Louise so wild and extravagant, Jeannine so limpid and bright; the two of them as like and unlike as two ivies that twine about the same tree but in opposite ways. Their voices: Louise's so grave, low, introspective, losing itself in her and desiring to be lost. Jeannine's so clear, so exact, threading the words and sounds and suddenly astonishing you by no longer being comprehensible—no single word can be made out, in spite of the thin, pure voice that goes on uttering, that rises in spirals and fades away in thin smoke.

Their arabesques, their alternating recitative that never stops nor tires: Milton's *L'Allegro* and *Il Penseroso*. And yet not the over-simple, too-perfect alternation of joyful and thoughtful; rather the low and the high, the deep and the shrill. The dark nightingale and the light, cruel lark. Two exercises in vocalization in different tones, two vertiginous trills dying in different ways. And yet both complementary to the same winged theme—flight.

Louise

The moment that I came into that room was an empty moment. Empty, unforgettably void of remorse, love, emotion. Empty. Have you ever come into contact with it, perfect emptiness?

Do you really know what it is, this draining away of everything that until the last few seconds had seemed to you a reason for being there, even if there had been an insufficient reason—love or desire or maybe revolt—but at least some kind of feeling; all

suddenly leaving you, and of course seeming so pointless, so irrele-
vant? The moment before, yesterday, some time back, you were
in the street; you knew who Etienne was and what he wanted
from you; your words and his formed a conversation. You wanted
a lover or you did not want one; you had met him and you either
tried to escape from him or else on the other hand you were
already making plans—marriage, perhaps; or if you were already
married, running off together. Or, at all events, love. The staircase
with its eau-de-Nil walls still meant something; and the woman
who opened the door to you was still a woman; already she had
no name left, no past, but her smile still lasted. Then this sudden
draining away: I went in, and the room was empty. I was with
Etienne and the room was empty. I was with myself and the room
was empty. Empty, empty; myself empty of myself. If the word
perfect has a meaning, I know that meaning. Empty, empty, perfectly empty.

*Her beautiful head leans back, falls back, pours back her dark
hair, which spreads out like a pool. No longer has she any face,
that rather too lovely face, too hard, great dark eyes, straight, flat-
bridged nose, the angle of the cheek-bone a little too distinct and
too severe, that face of a statue forgotten in a public garden (forgotten because it is too beautiful and so its beauty is not seen, and
because it finds the burden almost too much itself); her face pours
away with her hair and only her soft and rising throat, with its
murmuring stream of words, offers itself to the knife and flinches
from it. For she has fled, perhaps.*

I have fled?
"You can perfectly well love a man for his money," said
Jeannine. "Women are loved for their beauty, aren't they? Louis
is expecting me for lunch at the Berkeley. Will you come? Louis
will be well dressed. He will have a clean, well-groomed, English
kind of smell. He will have slept well in a soundless room. He will

not worry either about his suit, which will not have got creased in his perfect luggage (there is a special compartment in the suitcase, you know; it is very useful, it folds like this. It is rather bulky, of course, but . . .) or about the luncheon, which will be perfect too, or about his family, which he keeps at a prudent distance (the idea of a separate room for everyone being replaced by that of a separate flat for everyone, or a separate villa on the Riviera, or, when they are travelling, a separate suite—and the suites do not have to join, either), or about his well-cared-for body (even its little annoyances, after all, form part of his comfort. The scrupulous attention, the going to Switzerland for a rest from time to time, the cashmire scarf that he wraps round his delicate throat), or about his well-maintained soul. He reads good books in handsome editions, he has himself driven to exhibitions in his carefully closed, carefully sound-proofed car. He will turn his mind to nothing that he has not freely chosen, without either interference or obligation—he is a free man and he makes me share in his freedom.

I love the way he chooses his season, his time, his distance : Beirut might be a few hours' flight away or at caravan-distance. He is not even the prisoner of his own speed. On the contrary, out of a particular refinement, he will often choose other people's time and season : he will eat winter fruit in winter and buy jonquils in the spring. But what a difference there is in this voluntary agreement between his desires and their nearest, most natural object. He has chosen to love me. He has chosen to be faithful to me. I love him for his freedom."

Louise

I was gorged with meanings, responsibilities, choice. Not only the children, the daily food, but words—what am I saying? The eye's vision alone, a blossoming branch in spring, waving as I look in the warm breeze. I had to choose whether I should see it or not

see it, and the weariness of being pursued in this way wherever I
went, pursued by images and sounds and colours and words, of
being solicited, snatched at, urged by the pitiless and cannibalistic
existence of things, of being laid open by all my senses, sight, hearing, taste, touch, of being vulnerable through every pore and feeling, and with my mind and spirit flayed through having been so
long naked, as one's feet might be if one were perpetually forced
to walk without shoes.

I wanted no more of this unthinkable, scandalous weariness,
this insistence all round me, and I repudiated it, I thrust it from
me and with all my senses I would have nothing of it, closing my
eyes, my ears, dumb, deaf, blind, indifferent to love by night, eating anything that came to hand, saying anything or nothing,
obstinate, shut in, withdrawn all over, except through that crack
which would still open here or there, suddenly letting in a spur
of light, the piercing thrust of a sound, a word, an object, and
everything would start living again, would start hurting again over
my whole living surface, skin or soul or whatever you like to call
it, over everything I possessed that was capable of feeling pain or
of being hurt. Then Etienne, this room, and the rising cloudiness
that invaded me as I heard him lying. Lastly, the longing, the
longing for the void, for nothingness.

Jeannine

We decided to see one another on Wednesdays and Sundays.
We decided. Nothing compelled us. We could have done anything
we liked with the week. But we chose these regular meetings so as
not to be enslaved by our desires or our pleasure. We chose to do
what others do. On Sundays we chose to go into the country; we
chose the disagreeableness of crowds. A day the same as other
days, the same as other people's days.

We stopped just outside Paris, in the crowd. The windows were
shut, the sound-proofing was good and we listened to the concert

from the Salle Pleyel physically surrounded by the crowd, but to all intents and purposes surrounded by the crowd of those who were listening to the same concert at the same moment. The entire difference resides in this: we might have had an orchestra playing for ourselves alone; we might have chosen a day when there are no traffic-jams; we might have indulged in what the newspapers call 'millionaire's whims'. Of our own free will we chose to enjoy the life of the world in general, the faithfulness of the world in general, the pure water which is pure only because it is chosen. I love Louis because I choose to love him.

Pure water, Jeannine's pure face; pure, precious, her fine-drawn features that look as though they had been laid on by an inexpressibly light brush; a face that might have been soft and that is in fact only delicate; a face as gentle as a memory, a face whose very lips are pale, choose to be pale, perhaps to mock the pallor, the purity of those who have nothing left but shadow, whose shadow is their good, and whose shadow she takes away...

I should like to explain: I should like to tell Jeannine that you have no right to choose, that you deform, distort, dirty the splendour of chance, the splendid impetus; that you never reach the fortuitous heart of things. No, I should say, if it were not that I felt that the mere existence of this exact, fluid shadow were not enough to make itself and its condemnation clear. You have no right not to choose, no right to make game of the gift, the fine deliberate generosity. You have no right, I should say to Louise in the doorway of that room, if it were not that the lullaby she was singing under her breath was that wild arabesque, already written down. And what, in short, have I to do but to note her, to give her back her song and to give her life, being incapable of making its meaning understood; for if she does not carry within herself her own sense and meaning then it means that I have failed and that I must write another story.

entwined, their voices move away

"At last, the longing not to hear, not to understand, not to love. At last, for a moment, this emptiness, this rest, this abandoning of me by myself; this longing to be no more, this rest of no longer being, this dizziness of no longer being : the empty room, the empty words, the world without colour, without smell, without sound. Rest, death, myself emptied of myself. One more step, just one, and this emptiness for ever; one step, one more, into this void . . ."

"The windows closed, the crowd all round us, the crowd outside waiting (but still hooting, madly impatient, cursing—but silently for us, because of the perfect sound-proofing) and the crowd with-in, listening to the same notes, quivering, sighing, applauding the same notes—but invisible for us because of the everyday (and we have chosen it to be everyday) miracle of the radio; and in this crowd, our solitude in short, since we chose this double crowd, bringing it near or pushing it away as we wish, never submitting to it. And the fact that our perfectly ordinary position as isolated yet surrounded travellers on the N.12 or the southern motorway in the middle of all these assembled travellers and music-lovers, is, since we have chosen it, the exact equivalent of any other position whatsoever, however striking or remarkable (the back of an ele-phant or the top of Everest), that we should also have chosen—this freedom, this emptiness . . ."

Their voices move away with their themes entwining without touching in a fugue that is continually renewed, solved for an instant in a fleeting harmony that would be the end of a chapter (or of the chapter that is a book) and separating again, moving farther away, farther from me . . .

flight

So, by way of flight from God, the story of two women who

flee. Louise, thirty-five, with two little pig-tailed girls, a mathe-
matician as a husband (the poetry of mathematics, a theme I
love and one which I seize upon again with the pleasure of something one has repeated a hundred times). Louise, who has everything, takes a lover so as not to live this too perfect, over-endowed,
too dreadful life. The wrong that she does is for her good, since
wrong does not exist, whereas life, beauty, goodness, exhaust her
by existing too much.

She feels that she is being eaten up, is dying a little at every
moment from her husband's love, the wonder of her children, the
proliferation of things all round her that insist upon her love, her
amazement and her attention. She chooses the absurd so as not to
be exhausted. Death, in order not to die. But she will not succeed.
Before her eyes the most craven lover becomes a loving, suffering
creature—a man. She will love him and exhaust herself for him.
Louise may give up, or throw herself into debauchery. Underneath everything she will find herself again, still alive. "There is
no fleeing from the jealous God."

Jeannine, twenty-seven, blonde, vaguely a journalist, like everyone else, divorced, like everyone else, clear-minded, like everyone
else. It is she who coquettishly says *like everyone else*, and by that
she means *like all those people she chooses to know*. Jeannine
chooses her lover, her pleasures, her work; chooses, chooses,
chooses herself to such a degree that in the end she chooses nothing
any more except in relation to that character that she has become
to herself and that feels itself obliged to act, to dress and to love
'like Jeannine'. So with immeasurable zeal she runs away from
anything which, by a misplaced impulse, might make her swerve
—a longing for a dress, for example, or for a lover who might not
suit the Jeannine whom she has created. How she dreads and fears
herself, punishes and dominates herself! How she diets, shapes and
pares herself, Jeannine, that ascetic! By dint of choosing herself
she escapes from herself and no longer exists. Will she escape for
ever?

And what about me? I shall not escape, nor shall you, from that relationship which I have to establish between these two women. I shall not escape, nor shall you, from the result of that everlasting sum which the clerk who has lost something casts up despairingly again and again, always coming to the same total, the total that I shall always call the truth, that I shall always call God. And if I had written the story of these two women I should still not have been able to end it with a firm ending. Not so long as I myself had been unable to overcome my fear of the conclusion, of the last step, that fear which was so old that it dated from the time of the Emerald. And I wanted to overcome it. With all my strength.

Still, the work would have taught me resignation. That wonderful hope with which you begin a book, that vision in your mind of the perfect book, which lasts as long as the work goes on, as long as you are taken up with crossing out, recasting, doing over, as long as you have not reached that word finis which does not mean that the book is finished but that you have done all that you can for it. "A book is not finished," said Valéry, "it is forsaken." I did not want to have to forsake my life one day.

To conquer this fear of the captivity of choice. To reach a *final solution* of it (yet take note that this was Himmler's term for the extermination of the Jews). And as Alfonso the Pious, King of Portugal, observed on having the Ptolemaic system explained to him, "If the Creator had consulted me before setting about the task, I should have advised something simpler." I had reached that point. I was looking for something simple : conversion, for example. At the same time I was afraid of it. So I determined to drive a bargain with God. Truth should become my rule of life. I should apply it rigorously. It would be my system, my martingale. For this, God would surely overlook my shilly-shallying before the little formality of the purifying water and the register? I should be 'self-employed', as one is for family allowances. All right? A little wink heavenwards, and on we go.

I must admit that the results did not come up to all I had hoped for. I do not want to give more than one example, and that example is one that, odd as it may seem, dates from *after* that conversion that I found so hard to accomplish. One day when I was tired, distracted, I brought this system into action again, although I had left it off long before. You will appreciate all its touching absurdity

in three words

Interview.

"Are your characters for or against religion?"

"It is scarcely a question of for or against; I mean . . ."

"After all, you are a Catholic?"

"Yes . . ."

"Very well then."

He writes it down. He has no time to lose. He is a fair-haired young man of about twenty-three or twenty-four, very sure of himself, but not ill-natured, not aggressive. He is doing his job: speed, efficiency, civility. And patiently, exactly, he explains to me what it is that he wants—it is up to me to produce it.

"Something not at all vulgar, but which everyone can understand, you follow me? A popular article on the book and what it means, then you, your life, the connexion. Understand?"

"Yes, indeed . . ."

It is perfectly understandable, naturally. The book, my life, the connexion. I have ten minutes. My mind goes into a flat spin.

"I had put down two or three questions . . . Here we are. It ends with your heroine being converted, isn't that right?"

"Well . . . [slowly] I think that it is rather that she becomes aware that she is free to be converted or not to be . . . [I take off and finish in one gasp] and-her-conversion-consists-in-just-that-very-state-of-mind."

Well answered; that's the way. The young man's face expresses an austere satisfaction : he writes.

"Her conversion consists . . . Existentialist, eh?"

"I don't know."

"Pardon?"

"I mean I haven't read Sartre, except for his novels."

"So all these philosophers are humbugs?" He does not smile.

"I don't know . . ."

"Pardon?"

"I can't follow them."

"Why not?"

"I can't follow them."

His brow wrinkles.

"Yes . . . Very well. We'll leave that out. The personal angle. The connexion. Did you think of going into a convent?"

"Lord, no."

"Mystical crisis?"

"I don't know . . ."

He has the resigned look of a doctor whose patient cannot manage to explain his symptoms.

"Come now, I have to have something to tell them. Catholic upbringing?"

"No."

"Conversion, then?"

"Yes."

"Good. That's splendid, your conversion. When you try, you see." He writes down, *It was after her conversion that Françoise Mallet-Joris decided to write the life of Louise de La Fayette.* "Fine. That will do: I'll fix it. Now the personal angle. It's for a woman's paper so we have to have some psychology, some . . . What's your chief failing?"

"My . . .?"

"Chief failing. Don't get worked up. Writers are all asked that —you only have to say something or other, it doesn't matter what."

Something or other: but what something or other? I grope through a fog, and I find nothing but the truth.

"Impatience."

He laughs. He writes it down.

"Is that true or untrue?"

"True."

"Do you always tell the truth?"

"No; but I try."

"Why?"

"It is simpler."

"Odd, for a writer," says he, without dwelling upon it.

"Do you think that being a writer consists of telling lies?" The question does not please him. I am not the one to be asking the questions.

"It needs imagination, doesn't it?"

"But imagination is not lying."

"No?"

"No."

"Oh."

He looks rather staggered, and then cross, of course. What is more, I am wasting his time.

"Chief quality?" he says, sharply. I feel that he will no longer put up with the smallest outburst. We are not here to amuse ourselves, says his frowning forehead: I have my eye on you. Hurriedly I say "Patience."

"How funny."

He relaxes. I am not going to tell him that I did not do it on purpose, that in fact since I am naturally impatient and quick-tempered, my strongest effort is in the direction of restraining this impatience. It would be too complicated. And then it would be a pity to spoil everything just when he is willing to overlook my ludicrous observations. Age and Christian names of my children, my hours of work, favourite books and amusements (a certain hesitation at this point: I do not go in for amusements. To be

sure, I go to the cinema. I walk, I read, but in reality this is because I am tired at the end of five hours' work, and besides reading is my trade, too).

"Suppose we put *amusement: work*?" he suggests. "It would
be funny."

I feel a conscientious doubt.

"Would that not sound rather austere?"

"Yes. But then, after all, you are austere, aren't you?"

"Not in the least!"

He looks cross again.

"When you don't go out and don't dance, when you get up at
half past six and you find work amusing, then you are austere."

"Oh."

"That's the way it is." (He calms down, for he has the feeling
of having shut me up for good and all.)

"TV?"

"Not much good. Maybe *watches the telly with her children.*"

"Photography?"

"All right."

He looks at his notebook, weighs it up.

"It will do. You can tell your friends you weren't an easy one
to deal with."

"Really?"

"You ought to be used to it by now."

Yes, I ought. Yet I have never been able to get used to this two-
faced trap, this benign malignance, these frivolous questions that
are nevertheless serious, this ambiguous collaboration in a common deceit (underlying or open complicity: *they will like that*).

A possible way for this young man and me to talk might be at
the same time serious and scornful—each doing his job, pretending to take seriously things that are not serious, but which others,
the poor fools, will swallow with delight. Or else it would be all
of a piece throughout: myself talking nonsense to him and he taking it for nonsense and passing it on to the reader who does not

believe in it but who reads it to pass the time—for the very reason that he knows that it is nonsense, that it is harmless.

Complicity in any case, and a somewhat dubious kind of complicity. Am I there to utter harmless remarks? (But on the other hand there is nothing wrong with relaxation. If it amuses worthy souls to think that I like cooking on Sundays and to know how I make a *carbonnade* or *aïoli*, why not? That *too* is good, and it is part of life. Relaxation is good if it comes after work, sleep is good if it comes after waking and makes ready for it—and who, if not the individual, is to be the judge of *his* relaxation, *his* sleep?)

That day I was not uncomplicated enough to tell myself all this; I was all stiffness, fear, concrete, cement, everything you can think of that is utterly shut in. There are days like that, when you seem to have forgotten everything that you have so painfully learnt. At least I did have the excuse that I was not applying my heavy-handed reverence to my own person but only to words; for the using of words seemed to me both difficult and holy, all the more so that every day I saw them profaned and wrenched from their truth so very often that it literally hurt me—hurt me so much that I felt a kind of joy (and I still feel it) at the idea that the Nazis burnt books and that today the OAS imitates them. However negatively, the power of words is thereby recognized, and the magical ceremony of Nuremberg, with its great mediaeval piles of faggots, hallows the power of those it destroys.

And oh, how mediaeval I am myself, with my heavy, paralysing, pathetic armour, before this wretched dashing youth, so airy with his notebook, his scrap of pencil, his Tergal suit!

A spontaneous enmity springs up.

"So imagination is not the same as telling lies, eh?" he says in a sarcastic voice as he picks up his things.

"No."

My firmness vexes him.

"The fate of the world doesn't hang on the replies you make to *Marie-Claudine*, you know . . ." (he is growing coarse).

"I know."

"Don't you think you take yourself rather too seriously?"

At an earlier time we should have had a fine bawling row. It would have done me good, and him too. Perhaps a liking would have emerged from it. Who can tell, we might have seen one another again and become friends. Or else he would have gone, shouting that I was "an impossible person" (which is true) and slamming the door. Explanations? Long, complex, absurd. I already find it hard enough to explain me to myself, in three hundred pages. And then there is no time. And then tomorrow it will have to start all over again, with *Marie-Christine, Marie-Catherine, Marie-Madeleine* . . . With the maid, the children, my husband, our friends, the others, with my novel . . . I try cordiality.

"Don't you think that your chief failing may be impatience too?"

A somewhat strained laugh.

"Maybe. Have I irritated you?"

"Not in the least, I assure you. And I hope that I . . ."

"Of course not."

We pause for a moment between our dying hostility and a kindliness that is just ready to come into being. But there is no time to make things clear.

"I must run . . . Late . . . Double-parked—ticket . . . Glad to have met you. No hard feelings, eh?"

No hard feelings, of course. Where would you be if you were to go in for hard feelings just because you did not talk the same language. And yet in fact the unpleasant impression that remained with me after this interview, this particular malaise among the rest which had its own colour and meaning as if it were a 'theme', certainly did arise because young Tergal and I had each spoken our own language, a language adopted in each case to some degree by preference, to some degree by chance. Adapted, if you like, to our characters and our responsibilities, but both *equal*. In the presence of young Tergal I had behaved like one of those grown-ups I had admired when I was a child—people of whom it was said, "So-and-so will not do this, he is a Socialist, he is a Protestant, he is a Jew, he is rich, he comes from a family that . . ."

I had behaved like those grown-ups who *worked* so perfectly that everything looked as easy as one of those lovely inescapable sums about trains or taps : all you had to do was to find the point at which the lines called family, public opinion, character and so on, ran across one another, and thanks to this intersection, all behaviour, words and even the slightest detail of conduct could be deduced. Of course, from time to time the calculation had to be done over again : the fellow had settled down, had been ruined or converted to religion. Conversion then had the appearance of a natural upheaval (and basing myself upon the observations I heard I found it quite impossible to tell whether it was a blessing or a disaster); but although sometimes the sum had to be begun again from the beginning, at least the existence of an answer was never put in doubt.

Telling the truth, having decided that the truth was the best system and the one least subject to variation, I had therefore *worked* perfectly. But in his way, young Tergal had also worked. Communication between us had not been brought about easily. On the contrary, it had been made fundamentally impossible by the rigidity of the attitude I had taken up. Besides, in his way he too had displayed a good deal of inflexibility. If he had had more experience he would have pretended to go along with my whim; or rather, without even pretending, he would have talked my language by that kind of mimicry that makes some people, when they are talking to Englishmen, instantly take on an English accent. And if I had let myself go, could I not have adopted young Tergal's stylish scorn for what he obviously thought an inferior job that had to be carried out in an off-hand manner? If I had not yielded, then nor had he, with an equal degree of puritanism, given a single inch. We were both of us extremely young then. Perhaps after all young Tergal was very likable?

It all happened because that day I was tired. Tired of crossing out, amending, of truly existing. I was not serving the truth in which I believed; I was making use of it, turning it into a fortress to protect my weariness, my momentary refusal to live. And at once, with a magic rapidity, it *stopped being the truth*.

At a distance of years this commonplace interchange, long turned over in my mind, gave me the key to that dark night, to that temptation that I went through in a half-conscious state— the everlasting temptation of the void; or, to use a less solemn but more untrustworthy term, of sleep. Unable to deny to myself that God existed, and not daring to commit myself wholeheartedly, entirely, to this faith, I had tried to turn God into a machine. To make him take up a place in the catalogue. And (why not?) to devote myself to detective stories. As it happened I had a theme, a fine theme that had already been haunting my mind for some time. A theme with a sure-fire ending, a real psychological theme with a thunder-crash at the end and trumpets and a celestial apparition amidst the clouds. This theme was the story of

Major J.

Everything was coming into balance to allow me to deal with this subject I am speaking about. The fascination that I have always felt for stories of concentration-camps, torture and violence —horror and curiosity mixed : how is *that* to be explained or understood? Purely ideological indignation at the sight of the way the trials of the butchers were being carried out, this picking upon a few scape-goats who, they say, *gave the orders*, and who were shown in a glass cage before being put to death, thus setting free the conscience of all the worthy souls who merely obeyed the orders.

The interest that I feel in a certain type of character, people fashioned out of a somewhat thick kind of clay, rather heavy people, but thoroughly solid, thoroughly tangible, thoroughly in existence with all their idiosyncrasies and little ways, thoroughly shut up in the matrix of that body which is roused so slowly. Such a one was Major J., whose photograph I have before me now. Regular features, a lock of fair hair on his forehead, and in spite of his tribulations (the picture was taken during some sort of Nuremberg trial) a pleasant and still trustful look. This conscientious Teuton might be my brother, or my father. He was a Nazi officer and for a long while he was in command of extermination commandos. It is a face that astonishes you by its likable commonplaceness. And the anecdote comes pat for one who is talking about conversion. You shall judge for yourself.

Like many other people Major J. exterminated, since that was his trade. He exterminated Jews, gipsies, lunatics; he exterminated Poles, Russians, stateless persons. He exterminated soldiers (a comparative trifle), peasants, members of the Resistance, suspects, half-suspects, quarter-suspects; in a word, he exterminated men. Anything that came to hand, as you might say. What is odd about that, so far? What is there worth talking about? Nothing: I am coming to it. I said that he exterminated men, and I meant men in the restricted sense of the word. One day he was asked to add some no less suspect women and children to his list. A few more would not matter to Major J.: he already had three hundred thousand dead, both civil and military, to his credit. Well, Major J., whose chiefs had been thoroughly pleased with him up until then—Major J., who had carried out orders without a hint of reluctance or doubt, and who had carried them out with the most satisfactory results, now suddenly began talking about honour and conscience, and refused.

It is this moment in Major J.'s life that fascinates me. The image of this moment. This moment at which *honour* and *conscience* so strangely start showing themselves, having swallowed three hundred thousand deaths with the utmost cheerfulness. Suddenly it will no longer do. It is in vain that the most sensible arguments are brought against him—there are potential men among these children, and these women will bear other men who will turn into enemies, *racially suspect elements*. In vain they tell him that *he is illogical*; even this argument, which has such effect upon the Teutonic mind, does not convince Major J. Major J. refuses and goes off. You would think that this rather special kind of hero would die in front of a firing squad, thus atoning for his errors; that is how one would like it to end, and it would then make a fine moral tale. But not at all.

It is true that Major J. wrecked his career (and they say that for a soldier this is the highest pitch of heroism). He was sent to the Russian front, with the rank of corporal. It was a high price to pay for a few Jewesses who in any case would be exterminated by someone else. But he did not die. He had the further misfortune of being arrested by an American court which, taking his efforts into consideration (this pupil is not very highly gifted, but he does his best), let him off with ten years. Thanks to his good conduct—we should expect no less from him—he only had to serve six of them.

At present he is no doubt watering his garden somewhere in Germany. It is easy to imagine him taking refuge in farming, picking flowers, bringing up his sons (it is noteworthy that the proportion of individuals who loved flowers and children was astonishingly higher in the extermination commandos than in the ordinary army, in which there was a wealth of sour-pusses and misogynists. Liberation of repressions? May there not be a system here?) That is the end of his story. If his conscience and his honour make a second appearance, we shall know nothing about it. It is the first that interests me.

The first, and that face that I see from time to time in my mind's eye, a face with kindly features—those gentle eyes, for example—and somewhat uneven teeth (they had wanted to make him wear a brace when he was a little boy, but there was no persuading him)—a face which is after all very near my own.

You cannot possibly dream over Hitler's face, or Eichmann's:

they are too far from us, too much shut up in their closed, flat world, permanently cut off from ours. Whereas J., Hans Friedrich J. . . . Is it not an impulse that you yourself feel every day, that feeling that makes you say inwardly, *no, not that*?

You diddle the tax-gatherer, but you do not break and enter a bank. Or you break and enter a bank but you do not kill. Or you kill, but you do not torture. Or . . . It is in this way that each man sets his own limits and lays out a little personal conscience, as he might lay out a little garden in front of a suburban house, setting aside, in the midst of the grossest ignobility, a charming bed of scruples which allows him to judge his neighbours.

So it is not the mechanics of Major J.'s thought-processes that fill me with astonishment, but the fact that they should have worked so early, or so late. It is the exact moment at which they worked. *His face at that moment.* Did he hesitate for a long while before sending off that letter that asked for a transfer?

I can see him leaning over the rickety table whose ill-planed wood was rough under hand; maybe he even stopped for a minute to attend to a very small splinter that had stuck into his palm, pulling it out with an irritated tutting noise. Then he scratched his nose and rumpled his hair with his pen as he did when he was a schoolboy; and then he set himself to it, looking for excuses, making use of those huge German polite formulae that rise like the steps of a grand staircase at the bottom of which there stands the petitioner, at a respectful—and prudent—distance.

He must have turned this letter over in his mind a good many times in that spotless hut (kept very clean for the officers, but a wretched place for all that) by the office stove, in a little cold space reeking of smoke. Perhaps not far away there were men who were digging their own graves, men who had no time to examine their consciences. But for his part, he was deep in reflection. Would it be better to plead ill-health, or to mention his scruples? He was unable to prevent himself from referring, out of a kind of literary stylishness (who knows, maybe Major J. had the makings of a writer?), to 'the condition of his nerves, which were much affected by the painful requirements of his special duty'.

This harmless piece of vanity was his undoing: far more than his veiled refusal, this admitted squeamishness—of which perhaps he was secretly proud (I am not cut out for work of this kind, he must have said to himself, with the legitimate pride of an *intellectual*)—did him harm. Departure for the Russian front. Loss of rank. The mystery of this continuing life.

What interests me is this exact moment, and this wooden table, and the honour, and the hesitation: it might very well be called a conversion. Of course, one can imagine it otherwise—plain weariness, a physical sickening (the officer in charge of Auschwitz has left us a moving account of his disappointments and his difficulties in getting rid of the bodies of his awkward and cumbersome victims). It would be possible to imagine a kind of breezy good-humour in Hans Friedrich—"I'm fed up with these massacres!"—or a pride that rings false, imperfectly hiding a rising nausea—"I did not become a soldier to kill children!"

But as for me, I would rather have a simple uneasiness that has grown from day to day and whose close inspection has been put off, always put off until tomorrow, rather like a little toothache that one does not choose to notice out of fear of the dentist— then suddenly it is no longer bearable. You have to go through with it and you sit down at the wooden table (bawling "Is that writing-pad ever coming?" at your orderly; for you do not write often, whereas the orderly is perpetually scribbling on that over-thin paper—scribbling something or other: poetry, maybe) and write the letter, without any idea of mutiny (for you are not one of those who would even for a moment dream of running away or of rebellion: perhaps you are not even one of those who is sure he is right. But you *cannot go on*; that is all—you cannot go on).

With some degree of vanity or with none—no one will ever know—you write the words "nervous exhaustion", those words which are to turn a promising major into a brow-beaten corporal, and you quickly seal the letter, hurry to the post with it, and go to inspect the latest graves, inspect them without pity and even with a certain amount of ill-feeling against these nuisances, these victims who have just wrecked the career of a major under the Third Reich, Hans Friedrich J., a decent fellow with rather long hair, rarely in the habit of asking himself questions, and whose harmless face I have here before me as I write. Yes, that can certainly be called conversion. The moment at which the appearance of things changes. Or rather the moment at which one *allows* their appearance to change.

Before those moments the dead did not exist, the graves did not exist, the smell—that smell which drifted on that wretched east wind as far as the requisitioned villas where you listened to music in the evening—did not exist. Perhaps Major J., with his fair lock across his forehead (they used to check him for having his hair too long when he was a young SA, but that stage was long past), perhaps Major J. himself did not exist? Who knows whether he existed before those moments? And fundamentally when he wrote that letter, that blundering letter with its high-falutin phrases and a spelling mistake, he was not so much giving things the power of changing their appearance, as that of coming into existence, much as the suddenly-admitted toothache comes into existence. What intrigues me so and what turns this little-boy-executioner into my brother is that moment when at last he gives things the power to exist.

He too might say, "Before that moment I never thought." And it is true and untrue, little brother with the charming hair and the gentle mouth that said "Fire!" thousands of times.

But that moment came, as short and burning as lightning, as short and exact as a knife-stab, and it was all over, the sleeping, the ignoring, all over and finished, the listening to music for its own sake on fine execution-evenings. All over? At any rate that would be the end of this book, if I managed to write it. I left Hans Friedrich J. to his fate. After all, he had had that face, that moment, that lightning-flash : it was his business to make the best of it. To get through the war and the Russian front, the peace and the American court, life and prison and the suburban house, with this viaticum. I had given him his chance : what more could he ask? And why did he too refuse to give me the clear end, the full stop?

For he did refuse it me. He stayed there, motionless, at his wooden table, his letter written, without a single gesture or a word that would allow me to abandon him with no qualm of conscience. If he got up and went, as he must have done that evening (and for a few other evenings too, until his letter reached its destination, was examined and answered), to oversee the burial or the burning of the corpses with that ill-humour I have already spoken about (this loathsome drizzle really is the end!), with that veiled resentment (what a mess I am getting myself into for this riff-raff!), with that fear, that paralysing fear which now cannot but fill him, rush into him—not the fear of punishment, no, nor the fear of death, but the true fear, the only fear, that of feeling the growth within himself of that force which he had given the power to exist and which he called conscience, which he called honour, which I have called truth and which I *shall call God from now onwards.*

Thus everything brings me back to the same point, shying at the obstacle every time. And just as I do not write the story of Jeannine and Louise so I do not finish the story of Major J. Because it would be a bad book; and, what is worse, an untrue book. Because its end is a beginning. Because it is at the beginning of the book that the lightning ought to flash out and the trumpets sound, and because the continuation of the story is the dangerous progress in the darkness, the journey undertaken because of one's trust in the lightning-flash, the ceaseless effort that never ends, the road that stretches out for ever, and the rigid, unrelenting requirement that one has once, just once, acknowledged, imprudently acknowledged. . .

Because this letter that Major J. writes is the beginning of a story, and because this letter that I am sending to myself is the beginning of a story too, and one that I cannot, will not, dare not yet write. . . A story to which everything leads me back, a story that both ends and begins on a heavy June morning under the dusty chestnut-trees of the avenue Latour-Maubourg, a story in which each dawdling step that leads me nearer to the little chapel (time wasted in front of a shop-window peering at faded books; time wasted slowly pushing a stone along the gutter with my foot). Each hesitating, gloomy step ("Why, why am I really doing this?") counts, in which every moment of bitter distress fought against, overcome, springing from its ashes again ("Why, but *why*. . ." and at this moment alone among all the good reasons learnedly deduced there remains but one, the most limited, teeth clenched to conquer nausea, "Because I have made up my mind to it"). Each step, each moment of distress that brings me towards this limit, this threshold, this end, this beginning, to this life and this death commingled. . . .

If ever I knew what fear was, the most total physical and moral fear, doubt and nausea, repulsion, colic, absurdity, horror of the void, of all voids, then it was certainly on that particular day, standing in front of the windows of the bookshop in the avenue Latour-Maubourg, gazing at a shop-soiled copy of the Garnier edition of Virgil, a yellow volume with a stain at one corner; and it seemed to me that under my nail I could feel the grating, unpleasant touch of the stain.

I hope that Messrs Garnier will forgive me, but every time I see one of these books again a kind of sea-sickness comes over me once more, and I hurriedly look away. (In the same way, when I was a child I read a little illustrated tale throughout a long journey in a bus, in spite of my mother's advice—you can imagine the result; and for months I was unable to look at the wretched book without a heave.)

And the interval between that day when I wrote the word God,

when I established for myself the relationship between God and
that mathematical ecstasy, and that other day of the chestnut
trees was just this—a long journey in a

bus

Themes roughed out and at once abandoned. Sudden rebel-
lions; utter prostration. To God : "You owe everything to me,
since I give you being", then moving without a pause from fury
to terror, "I owe you everything, since I owe you my feedom"
Raging, passionate arguments. And then suddenly an easing of .
the pressure and a few days of blessed rest, sleep, unawareness.
Everything delightfully absurd once more. Wonderful strolling
through the town, wonderful juxtapositions of shop-signs, windows, phrases in the underground, picturesque faces, little inex-
pensive dresses, newspapers, films, more films—the writing down
of that, decorative art, a blessed relief : artificially rediscovered
childhood, and the now slightly depraved delights of putting in
the colours. . . The patience wrenched rather out of shape ("it
will come right"), attention somewhat turned aside, dwelling on
the surface of things ("there is a Time for writing, and a Time for
watching"), violence knowingly directed towards very limited
objects. . .

But no book ! No baby deformed by this thalidomide ! Beloved
work that would not let itself be hoodwinked ! If it had served
only for that end and no more it would still have earned my everlasting loyalty. Dear unyielding, infuriating work, dear lack of
facility which did shackle me, and which does shackle me now
to this table until, whether I like it or not, I shall have found the
words that have a meaning, for I do not possess the art of handling the other kind. It was necessary that I should let myself be
hurried away by it, jolting, lurching, shaken in every direction,
cursing it and yet clinging to it nevertheless, and carried along,
always farther along, in spite of distress and sickness. . .

For it insisted upon that. For the logic of my work insisted upon that. For, as in the choice of a theme, I had to balance the picture and the caption, the choice of my nature (that share of the inexplicable, of grace and of poetry that belongs to certain places, certain themes, certain faces), and the choice of my will (certain things that had to be said, to be communicated, and which were essential to me), and finally for this choice of a life (to have let it drift in absurdity would have been a choice too) I had at last to commit myself totally, not only by my mind, by my heart, but by every one of my motions, even the most material of them, by the whole of my daily existence, which would then become, as by the help of those little words that are so hard to grasp, a subject becomes the theme of a book, entire, with both picture and caption, grace and will—so, I say, would my existence become a *life*.

Thus I should not escape from that last and first step. As a theme that still belongs to me turns into a book and escapes from me, so existence, dedicated and given, would escape from me. And as I hold back for a moment at the threshold of a book— suppose I am wrong after all, suppose this theme is not *my* theme, this way of speaking not *my* real style, this balance not *my* balance : it is so easy to be mistaken and I commit myself entirely for two years—so at the threshold of that life which begins when one chooses it, I still hold back a moment, just one moment. And as I always do when fear takes on the pleasing mask of thought, I call up the comforting face of days of weariness, the pure, kindly face of

Theo

Theo. The smallest child, the child one takes by the hand to feel less alone. The child who stumbles a little on the tow-path because one's steps are too long for him. Who pipes away at random without listening to our solemn confidences. Who picks up a stone, raises his head to follow the flight of a bird—but who, when we stop and sit down on the bank of the canal and gaze over this melancholy landscape, this flat country with here and there a barge or a bicycle, both on the same level, already possesses the same attentive, rather saddened eyes and the patient gentleness of the unhappy days to come in Paris.

Theo. A humble, unrebellious life, the life of a painstaking employee, a good son, a good father: Theo getting off the train in Paris to sell pictures, still wearing the too-long frock-coat of his own country and speaking with its heavy accent; and the long-suffering heavy sweetness of the poorer sort, and the wonderful blind trust of love. . .

Theo, who earns his living so meagrely, who climbs the ladder rung by rung, saves his money, follows the humble beaten track step by step, as before he followed the tow-path of the canal. . .

Theo, whose entire strength is exhausted by this stream of little simple, awkward letters that go off, with a fifty- or a hundred-franc note, towards Arles, carrying peace, tenderness and confidence to the immense being who is doing battle with colour. Theo does not experience this intoxicating anguish; Theo does not gradually go mad from exhaustion and tension. Theo does not write wonderful ardent letters that will be read in anthologies. How few of the editions will include, together with those of the painter of *The Crows*, the letters of his modest brother—although the painter said, "You are the joint author of my works. . . I paint with you. . ." How few people linger over these letters which are all the same, over this long monotonous plain-song, monotonous with the wonderful monotony of faith.

Vincent goes on with his terrible fight which cannot have an end, as he has always known (ever since the time of his ministry, when, dressed in rags and sleeping in a shed, he already dreamt of giving himself wholly, all at once—and he so awkward with his big body and his violent clumsy love). Vincent goes on wrestling with the angel, goes mad, recovers, his ear cut off, the sunflowers, the asylum, Auvers. . . stages along a Calvary described and thought over a hundred times.

Theo too goes on living. He does not fight; no. With the good will of a studious but not over-gifted child, he tries to live like everyone else, to have a pleasant little flat, to look after himself. He marries, he has a child—isn't that how you do it?—and goes on writing letters, sending money, what money he can. When Vincent's battle finishes, Theo is exhausted. His health is exhausted, his strength is exhausted. He is never to know the happy mediocrity of the pleasant little flat, the better job, the child growing. His life has been a long blood-giving, and it has undermined him—and his work too has come to an end. He has no need of anything now but of rest in that twin grave at Auvers, that grave on which the pilgrim's gaze does not linger.

I have longed to write an *On the Tomb of Theo van Gogh,* as one formerly did for those one admired. But no doubt he would not have liked it. How can one commend, what praise can one offer, confronted by that self-denying love, so pure that it only took form through the man who was its object? The admiration that one gives to the sunflowers goes also to Theo's patient love.

I love this sweet gentle-scented love, so shamefast and so domestic. I love it because it is a love of my own country (within a few miles, but we will not quibble over a frontier), one which I see surrounded by those ceremonious, touching green plants that you see behind the small window-panes of the ugly little Dutch and Flemish houses. I imagine Theo sitting down to coffee and bread and butter with that punctuality that we inhabitants of the flat countries take with us everywhere. I see him choosing the wall-paper for his flat with that thorough trust in life that no disappointment can dispel (we are so used to winter!), and perhaps writing those letters which drained away his life, writing them every day at the same time, looking at the big watch lying on the table before going off to 'the shop'. No, this exhausting, monotonous love is not a battle—it is a battle-weapon for another, who would have collapsed at his first encounter without it.

Theo's kindly face; Vincent's face too, of course. There is no separating the one from the other. That is what makes me love them so. One continually goes from the one to the other, and their relationship. . . I still go back to it. I shall always go back to it. To those two twin graves whose mystic meaning is always apparent to me. Will it be believed that if I wished to give this narrative (such a difficult narrative to write) a protector, to set a tutelary figure—or a *patron saint*, as they say—on top of it, I should choose Theo van Gogh?

And yet before writing its final words—before going beyond that shop-window to which my eyes are fixed as though in desperation—I have to have yet another patron. For the double face of Theo and Vincent is only the symbol of that harmony towards which I am obliged to strain without any hope of attaining it upon this earth. And since in order to write my book I have both to form an idea of what its perfect state would be, and to resign myself to never reaching it, that quest for harmony which is so well symbolized by the two graves at Auvers still lacks a resignation that is also a hope—it lacks the equivocal face, as imperfect as we are ourselves, the face of

Léonie

Léonie Martin, with her unfavoured Christian name; Léonie, whose memory is rather sickly too, all overshadowed as it is by the brilliant presence beside her of her sister Thérèse who, having become Theresa of Lisieux no longer has a surname: Saint Theresa.

Léonie, sister of Saint Theresa. Sister throughout eternity. Unfavoured fate.

Neither mother nor wife, Léonie: a nun, too. A nun, and the sister of a saint. The impossibility of equalling—what am I saying, the impossibility of ever coming near the little Carmelite. What about her other sisters? But Léonie suffered more than Pauline, the young saint's 'little mother', more than Céline, her favourite sister, and more than Marie, the eldest and the prioress. Léonie, pierced through with doubts and various longings, unable to imagine any other *order of perfection* than that of the monastic life, which since she was a child she had had pointed out to her as the highest, resigning herself, pulling herself together again, leaving one convent for another, and once more joining a religious order for good. Joining it outstripped and beaten in advance: Léonie must have suffered more than all of them.

Little is known about Léonie. The biographers have naturally concentrated all their attention upon the Little Rose. She is one of those fleeting shapes, lost like those one sees at the window of a train as it leaves, or on the road when one is oneself the prisoner of a car. Or that nameless face of a portrait in a provincial museum, *attributed* to some obscure painter and keeping its secret in the shadows . . . That enmity which she felt as a child for a maid-servant, that uneasiness of her mother (the pious, charming Zélie), that violence that one guesses at, those hesitations before going into a convent that were piously smothered by her parents and of which only a faint echo has come down to us, and then her decision and those words with which the matter is closed— "She was a good nun". Mysterious, yes, mysterious Léonie. An escaping face, a Botticelli face, poetic and sad, rather sickly, rather confused.

What answers were there for Léonie? Finding another form of perfection, another order of truth whose road would not seem barred to her. Or, on the contrary, deriving a fresh vocation, a new, more perfect humiliation from the certainty of failure—the vocation of imperfection, the acceptance of imperfection . . .

Yes, Léonie would be quite a good patron for a novel.

another one

Since it is laid down that I am going to write a novel. Another one, as Lucien puts it. You have courage, says Luc. A novel in which there will be no question of my distress, nor Algeria, nor of the bringing up of children, nor of truth, nor of the death of a friend that is saddening me now whilst I write these pages. Nor of God. A novel that will deal with nothing, but in which everything will play a part, like the food that I eat, the air that I breathe, and which, in short, makes up my *self* as much as my love for truth does, and my faith in God.

God himself will be neither more nor less, in this book, than sustenance, nourishment absorbed, the substance of my blood, part of my ego. God will not be the murderer. I shall not make use of God to write this book; but I hope that God will make use of me.

A book. It does not matter what book. A love-story, or the story of a man who writes his diary, or the story of a girl who goes into a convent . . . It hardly matters. Any theme at all, just as I feel that I might be anyone at all. A mere datum, like one of the data of a problem. An unescapable datum, of course. At this moment there is only one possible subject, just as there is only one me. The same datum, before and after the conversion. The same, and yet . . . Come, I see that I shall have to reach this moment, that with the utmost simplicity and, in short, with the fewest possible precautions, I shall have to come to that day when I was going along under the stifling chestnut-trees of the avenue Latour-Maubourg, with my everlasting distress thoroughly with me, and that despair of living that made me say over and over again, "It must be stopped; I must put an end to *this*."

And *this* is the body's revolt, the supreme wrenching back, the refusal to be a whole, a single being, the longing to escape even if it is only for a single moment longer, from the crushing responsibility of being oneself . . . Lucien, you said "It is very convenient, having faith" : would you have gone over that threshold? I did.

I did it with disgust and with repulsion. Dusty chestnut-trees,

the oppressive heat of June, the oppressive silence of the fashionable parts of town, empty at eleven o'clock, that I should have
liked to run away from! Farewell certainties, hopes and even
temptations! There was nothing left but that stupid and animal
courage which makes you face up to things and which is rightly
called the courage of despair. "If I do not do it today, I shall
never reach this point again." And again, "For I have determined
upon it." I went up the steps. What then? The chapel, of course,
and all that—candles and words slowly spent. It has all been described a hundred times over—so worn and so new. And myself,
a stranger to my own will, undergoing the unimaginable torment,
hearing my own voice utter the unimaginable words. "Do you
renounce . . . ?" "*I do renounce.*" "Do you believe . . . ?" "*I do
believe.*" Are other details really necessary?

Afterwards, the avenue just the same; and the shop-window.
And inside me, the silence that attends cataclysms. The long waiting for the underground, legs strangely weak. From time to time,
with a feeble, unlasting pride, these words in my head: "I have
done it." Silence again; a bomb-ravaged town, or the padded
deafness of convalescence. This was to go on for several days.

Words, the children, my numb hands that drop things. The un-
reality of my room, my voice, the milk boiling over that scalds
my finger. Oh! I look at it, at my finger, and suddenly, "*But what
am I waiting for?*"

Then all at once the avalanche, the overflowing (there too) of
the thoughts, the feelings, the uneasiness, of everything since the
beginning and I am shaken to the very soles of my feet by this
whirlwind, this loving and violent and (why not?) bantering
grasp, and this time this is it, it is the trumpets, the tearing veils,
the rope that breaks, the *thunderstroke* : and I do not mind if the
metaphor is worn, because it is *not* a metaphor and because the
person who has been struck by lightning does not care about sta-
tistics nor about knowing how many people have been struck
before him. And these portentous words within me, around me,

even on the kitchen wall that has cracks running down it and which could do with a good wash : *nothing more.*

Nothing more. For the first time, nothing more to wait for—no more alibis, pretexts, magic objects : nothing more except inside me this sudden frightening power to live, to live at once.

Nothing more between me and that chasm, my absolute freedom. No more walls, partitions, between the morning me and the evening me, the me declaring God without living God. A sudden coming together of the whole being, of all those cogs that had for so long been working separately, turning in emptiness. No more walls separating the children's room from the writing room, the thinking room from the room for living. A single freedom, a single unity throughout. A single battle, and always the same, in which it is forbidden even to expect victory. The sudden dizziness of this outlook.

But hope begins where expectance stops. This evening and tomorrow will be like the other days; the same words, the same tasks, perhaps the same failures. But the whole flooded by peace : not the peace of answers given, the peace of no answers. A living peace, one that accepts life's imperfection. You are not dead, you old longing for gardens of Eden and for machines, old temptation to founder, to abdicate; you will reappear. But you will only be a temptation, never a goal any more at all. We have just renounced machines. There will be no machine for living instead of us, even if it is decorated with a splendid name. Even if the machine bears the name of God.

Take the floor-cloth; mop up the spilt milk. Get the supper ready, and tomorrow patiently write one word, a second word, a book, *another one.* Only yesterday, when I was still clinging to the stubborn illusion, I said to myself, "after this step, everything will be changed." Nothing is changed, except this power within me which was always there, but which I had to accept before it could belong to me. Nothing has changed, but I am *capable* of changing everything. Nothing is changed, but God in me can change every-

thing, since I accept it. Wonderful, frightening discovered freedom. No, possessing faith is not convenient. You still have to live
it: as you say of a book that you are dreaming about, it still has
to be written. And upon this it depends whether the dream shall
remain a dream or become a living reality.

Here, as at the threshold of a book, the possible explanations
come to an end. If the book has no meaning, what is the good of
explaining it? And if it is alive, it stands on its own. Is not one
more book, one more life, a sufficient proof of faith? Live, then,
and write. But then why the two years spent on this reflection,
which has not yet become a novel?

These two years spent on this somewhat naïve picture-book,
which can only give pleasure to children, rather sick children who
have the habit of patience and who gently turn the pages without
tearing them, sometimes going back, and who go to sleep with
their hand upon a picture that will follow them to the other side
of the looking-glass . . .? No doubt it is because it is the book that
I should have liked to read when I was a little girl in my attic-
bedroom that I finish writing it here in this room, which is also
an attic. For the only child who wanted this book, and who, in
order to have it, had to write it. But no doubt we all of us write
this book in our own manner, and that every day.

In vain? There again, there is no answer. The only possible
answer is one that was given me by one of my dear concierges.

She was an old, dirty, poor woman, with no notion of hygiene,
wonderfully fierce, neither asking anything of anyone nor giving
it, stiff with pride and stuffed with stupidity; and it was she who
taught us this lesson. We went to see her after a death which had
left us very unhappy and low in our spirits. She insisted upon
having an account, which only made our sadness worse. "Did he
suffer much? Did he know he was dying? What were his last
words? Is it true that . . .?" We protected ourselves as well as we
could against this breaking in upon our feelings, which we thought
out of place. But our attempts at turning the conversation were

in vain. With that shameless pertinacity of the old she perpetually brought us back to the death-bed which we wanted to leave. "It seems that he had got terribly thin? Did the doctor operate? Did he talk right up to the end?" My husband, exasperated by this continually and, as it were deliberately, renewed pain, could not resist saying to her, "Do you think it really does any good, going over all this?"

It was so obvious to her that she gazed at him in astonishment. "Why, of course it does," she said firmly. "These things have to be said."

"But don't you see how it hurts . . ."

"All the same, just tell me . . ."

"But what's the good? It's so pointless."

She thought about it for a moment, an old pythoness surrounded with shawls, hot-water-bottles, ill-smelling tisanes, obscure traditions that came out of dusty cupboards on holidays. She weighed the pros and the cons fairly and without pity, with all her experience as midwife-cook-layer-out, the jealous holder of forgotten and useless secrets, and finally she gave her considered judgment: "That may be so. But for all that, these things have to be said."

We knew very well that there was nothing to be added. The shadow of what is holy had just moved through this evil-smelling slum. Pointlessly and at length we set ourselves to giving an account of all that had happened.